Klingon Drinks

BLOODWINE   Do not confuse this drink with Regullan Blood Wine. Klingon blood wine is fermented from the roots of the Tso plant.

The Tso plant drinks no water. It leeches blood from passing animals and Klingons. Klingon bloodwine contains blood. The strong wine tastes sweet, with a slightly metallic aftertaste. Color depends on the region of origin. It can range from blood purple to transparent pink in color. This drink should not be missed.

BLACK ALES   There are several commercially available black ales. Black ales should be served warm or piping hot. The syrup of *gfai* beans is fermented with grains to create the black drink. The syrup carbonates the liquid. The ales taste bitter on the tongue, but deliver an extraordinarily sweet aftertaste. Commercial varieties are the dregs of the cask mixed with black colored water. They don't taste the same as a private stock. If you cannot avail yourself of a private stock do taste a public one.

KLINGON SALT WATER   Most races should drink a chaser with Klingon salt water. The drink is made of sea salt and tuber alcohol. The salty drink is very strong, approaching 200 proof. Without a sweet, syrupy chaser, most races will choke on this Klingon delicacy. It is highly recommended.

KLINGON GREEN DRAGON   This drink is no longer made. Several thousand five hundred gallon casks remain on the homeworld. The origins of this drink are unknown. In its pure state it also makes a good solvent.

Drinkers of pure Green Dragon often remark that it numbs the lips and tongue. Partakers often fail to notice how much this drink burns their esophagi and stomachs. It must only be drunk in diluted form. A twelve-to-one ratio renders it safe. The drink offers an unforgettable experience.

MORE INSIDE!

QUICK TIPS

◢ Klingon Foods

ZENTAUR HAUNCH The meat is similar to lamb and not native to Klingon. The Zentaur, or Zentari, as they call themselves, are considered sentient beings within the Federation. Eating Zentaur is a crime for Federation citizens.

The meat is cooked with the leaves and roots of the Toragh plant. The leaves dissolve into a fine sauce. The roots are served on the side.

BOILED TARGSHEAD SOUP Most tourists are familiar with targs. This soup is a festival dish. It is served at Consortship Ceremonies, Rites of Inclusion and Ascension Anniversaries. Fortunately for tourists, these events are daily occurrences. Unfortunately they are private festivals. A visitor must be accompanied by a Klingon.

The targs head is thrown into a vat of boiling oil. It is cooked until the meat is reduced to a liquid. It is then removed from the fire. Several root vegetables are thrown in. After cooling, it is passed around in a large bowl. Each celebrant drinks as much as he can. This dish highly recommended.

QIRTS This fish lives around a large volcanic vent in the ocean off the coast of the Broken Land. They are found in no other location. They swim in circles around the vent sucking in abundant microscopic life. Once a Qirts begins to circle, it always swims in one direction. One side of its body atrophies while the other grows muscular.

Qirts are harvested when the cooked fishes float to the top. This dish is hard to find outside the Broken Land. Several restaurants in Throne City import it and charge exorbitant prices. To sample this dish, go to Qortazh on the Street of Warriors. He's the only one who leaves the tendrils on; the tendrils are the best part.

QUICK TIPS

♪ Foods to Avoid

BEETLH   Avoid any dish with this ingredient. Beetlh is a virtually indestructible Klingon pet. They are eaten when they die. Beetlh die when their bodies fill with spawn.

Dead adult Beetlh are eaten by passing scavengers. Eating them is fatal. Beetlh spawn gestate in the stomach of the unwary scavenger. When gestation is complete, the infant Beetlh eat their way out of the host. One runs the risk of being eaten by one's dinner.

BLUE VEGETABLES   The blue color of these vegetables comes from cyanide in the cellulose structure of the plants. These vegetables are poisonous to many species. Klingon tea is made from a blue plant. Many races drink an antidote with it.

'RROTMEY   These mall fried grubs look like brown spheres. They are difficult for tourists to avoid. The suffix "-mey" in their name means "scattered all about." The finger foods are served at any Klingon gathering.

The delicious food is the nearest Klingon equivalent to Terran "popcorn." Much of their flavor comes from acid. The acid produces a pleasant, warm feeling in Klingons. It burns a hole through the stomach lining of non-Klingons. While not immediately fatal, *rrotmey* cause great pain. Unless medical attention is immediate, a handful of Klingon "popcorn" will be the last thing you eat.

MORE INSIDE!

UNAUTHORIZED AND UNOFFICIAL

LET'S TREK

The Budget Traveller's Guide to

KLINGON WORLDS

James Van Hise
Hal Schuster

PIONEER BOOKS INC

Recently Released Pioneer Books...

TO ORDER CALL TOLL FREE: (800)444-2524 ext. 67
credit cards happily accepted

Library of Congress Cataloging-in-Publication Data
James Van Hise, 1959—
Hal Schuster, 1955—

　　Let's Trek: The Budget Traveller's Guide to The Klingon Worlds

　　1.　　Let's Trek: The Budget Traveller's Guide to The Klingon Worlds

　　　　　(television, popular culture)
　I. Title

Published by Pioneer Books, Inc., 5715 N. Balsam Rd., Las Vegas, NV, 89130.

First Printing, 1994

PUBLISHER and DESIGNER: Hal Schuster
COVER ART BY Bruce Wood, COVER DESIGN BY Hal Schuster

GUIDE TO THE PHOTOS (in order of appearance)

NAVY KLINGON MILITARY OFFICER
　　　Photo © Michael John

FEMALE KLINGON NAVY OFFICER
　　　Photo © Michael John

BAT'TELH (Hand made by Steven J. Frey)
　　　Photo © Steven J. Frey

The Klingon Agonizer (Hand made by Steven J. Frey)
　　　Photo © Steven J. Frey

Klingon Disruptor and Agonizer
　　　Photo © Steven J. Frey

Steve Frey and Daughter, Kathryn Frey (7 weeks old) as original series Klingons.
　　　Photo © Laurie Browne

Steve Frey as "Kahless"

Steve Frey as original series Klingon

A 24th century Klingon
　　　Photo by J. Van Hise

A Klingon warrior with pain stick following an Age of Ascension ceremony.
　　　Photos by J. Van Hise

A 24th century Klingon at Age of Ascension ceremony.
　　　Photo by J. Van Hise

Admiral Keel Epetai K'ta'ri of the Klingon Strike Force (Actually David L. Christensen)

K'Torak (Vaughn Pickett) and QelDaS (Paula Pickett)
　　　—Klingon warriors of the Imperial Military

Imperial Klingon warrior QelDas zantai-Qlavaq
　　　Photo © Vaughn Pickett

Klingon woman QelDaS
　　　Photo © Andy Pischalnikoff

QelDaS Qlavaq and Kalt Amitai, Imperial Klingon warriors.
　　　Photo © Vaughn Pickett

QelDaS the Freebooter
　　　Photo © Vaughn Pickett

Female "Romons" (Klingon/Romulan half-breeds). actually Jenifer Lineker & Judy Pischalnikoff. [Make-up by Andy Pischalnikoff]
    Photo © Andy Pischalnikoff

A Klingon civilian
    Photo © Dorothy Truslow

A Child's Victory!
    Photo © Jack Krolack

The Klingon woman QelDaS
    Photo © Andy Pischalnikoff

Admiral Qlavaq and Kh'Lan Treveq. Qlavaq is holding a Bat'telh.
    Photo © Vaughn Pickett

Tatsuki, Khalil, QelDaS, Kinraj and Maelen
    Photo © Vaughn Pickett

A Klingon Freebooter
    Photo © Vaughn Pickett

QelDaS zantai-Qlavaq, an Imperial Klingon warrior
    Photo © Vaughn Pickett

Keetaj and Mak'chu giving QelDaS the Rite of Ascension ceremony.
    Photo © Margaret Mosby

An alluring Klingon lady!
    Photo © Dorothy Truslow

"A Child's Victory" costume creation by QelDaS which won "Best Master" at Westercon '91.
    Photo © Jack Krolack

"Klingons Hate Tribbles!"
    Photo by Don

Klingon Navy female military officer.
    Photo © Michael John

QelDas
    Photo © Expressly Portraits

UNAUTHORIZED AND UNOFFICIAL

LET'S TREK

The Budget Traveller's Guide to

KLINGON WORLDS

INTRODUCTION

TRAVEL TIPS

The first time traveler, especially one from a planet with little off-world traffic, will be astounded by the variety of unusual people that populate the galaxy. A few simple tips will guide the new traveler dealing with aliens for the first time:

Always mind your manners.

Never assume your manners are the alien's manners.

Always keep your eyes and your mind open.

Here's a quick survey of some of the non-Federation aliens.

EXTREME INDIVIDUALS   The peoples of the galaxy vary greatly.

The Halkans are pacifists, among the most agreeable people in the galaxy. Don't be fooled by their pleasant manners. They will refuse to budge on a point of principle. They refuse to export dilithium crystals to the Federation, even though they are plentiful on their world.

The Ferengi are avaricious. It is almost impossible to avoid Ferengi merchants and con men.

There continue to be many conflicts in space. The Tellarians, a patriarchal species with strong family units, recently ended a war against the Federation. The honorable species rescues stranded travelers. They are hospitable in a brusque way, but their accommodations are severe and their food bland. They adopt abandoned children of other species, and are clearly not xenophobic.

Cardassians may be encountered near Bajor and the Denorios Belt. They engaged in a long war with the Federation until an armistice was signed and the Cardassians withdrew from Bajor. It is a fragile peace. Travelers encountering Cardassian vessels are advised to avoid all contact. Cardassians encountered on Federation worlds are not a threat, although often arrogant and overbearing. Cardassians in contact with the Federation are members of the military; their personality may not be representative of all Cardassians. Cardassians are a warrior race, colder and more calculating than Klingons, and thus potentially more dangerous. Recent intelli-

INTRODUCTION

gence reports reveal a growing anti-militarism that the Cardassian High Command is attempting to crush.

UNLIKELY POSSIBILITIES Some rarely sighted galactic civilizations are almost mythical. The Douwd may have reality-altering mental powers. Reputed to be similar to the Q in abilities, they do not share that race's interest in Terrans.

Little is known of the origins and motivations of the "Q." One is notorious for frequent intrusions into Federation affairs. He has referred to a "Q Continuum," leading to expostulation that they dwell in a parallel dimension that borders on our own. They may be energy beings in their natural state. The species seems to be testing humanity, but their motivations are unknown.

Some species offer little basis for communication. The distant Shelius star system is the home to a race known as the Sheliak Corporate. The crystalline life forms speak a completely unknown language. They have grasped the basics of several Federation languages, enough to agree to the Treaty of Armens after one hundred and eleven years of entreaties. They have never met with Federation emissaries in person, so their general appearance remains unknown.

RECLUSIVE AND ELUSIVE The Jarada, or Harada, are an insectoid species possessed of a complex language. History records that the first Federation ambassador to contact them incorrectly pronounced a greeting. The greeting was simple to the Jarada, but mind-numbingly complex to humanoids. The Jarada were so offended they withdrew from contact for decades, finally agreeing to another diplomatic approach after ignoring all Federation messages for years. Fortunately, Captain Jean-Luc Picard of the USS Enterprise mastered the greeting, and so a limited diplomatic exchange with the Jarada has finally begun. The Grizellas, another far-flung species, are even more approachable— although since they hibernate six months out of their year (which is close to a standard Terran revolution) it might be necessary to time a visit properly. They are a party to the Treaty of Armens, distant neighbors of the Sheliak Corporate.

There are rumors and legends of species few believe exist. In the case of the planet Aldea, the myths turned out to be essentially true. A world-wide computerized shield concealed this planet located in the Epsilon Mynos system. The world suffers from nearly complete ozone depletion. Since the removal of the shield the Aldeans have become accessible to the outside universe. They are struggling to rebuild their population and welcome tourists and colonists.

The T'Kon Empire also turned out to be real. The ancient culture, which once ruled much of the Milky Way galaxy, has been extinct for six hundred thousand years. Underlining the mortality of civilizations, ruins can be found scattered on desolate, abandoned worlds.

ORIGINS OF THE GALACTIC PEOPLES Many humanoid races owe their existence to an incredibly ancient, greatly advanced, *ur*-humanoid species. The race seeded primordial oceans of many worlds with genetic codes. A single message from this species, the most ancient hologram known, has been deciphered. Their form and voice echoes across billions of years to address their descendants.

This race may be the Preservers, whose existence had previously been expostulated. Several worlds contain obviously transplanted human populations and protective devices beyond the technological capability of their inhabitants. The devices are designed to ward off dangers from space. The connection of the *ur*-humanoids to the Preservers is conjecture, and the artifacts of the Preservers are much more recent than the *ur*-humanoids are believed to be.

Recently, the Wadi, a race native to the Gamma Quadrant, passed through the Wormhole. The strange, mysterious, game-playing aliens are only one of the recent species to appear. The galaxy brims with new discoveries every day.

BLACK CLUSTERS This phenomenon was recently revealed. The easily detected clusters generate a powerful, destructive graviton wave front feedback in response to the presence of a starship's shields. This can be avoided by passing through the cluster with shields disengaged. Before this discovery, it was possible for a starship to suffer severe loss of life and even destruction from the graviton wave feedback. Black Clusters occur throughout the galactic rim.

Long shrouded in mystery, in the decades since the armistice was signed, the history, culture and beliefs that make up all that it means to be a Klingon have gradually become known and understood. This book is the first comprehensive look inside that Empire. These pages travel from the homeworld Qo'noS (pronounced "kronos") back through history to the origins of its many clans and historical figures and beyond into the levels of Klingon culture and heritage.

For people planning to visit the Klingon Empire, and in particular the Homeworld, information is presented on the planet, its climate and seasons and food and drink. Night life receives special coverage.

The philosophical history of the Klingons is presented in a variety of forms, including the background of Kahless, the only legendary figure whose significance was accepted by every clan on the Homeworld. The recent "return" of Kahless still elicits much speculation and surmise outside the Klingon Empire, but has been almost universally embraced within the Empire.

Religions of any indigenous culture met by Federation travelers should always be respected unless life-threatening elements present themselves. The planet Rotiss, and its belief in worshipping, washing and eating the first guest met in each lunar cycle led to considerable distress due to poor

---

A NOTE TO OUR READERS

The information for this book is gathered by researchers during the late spring and summer months. Each listing is derived from the assigned researcher's opinion based upon his or her visit at a particular time. The opinions are expressed in a candid and forthright manner. Other travellers might disagree. Those travelling at a different time may have different experiences since prices, dates, hours, and conditions are always subject to change. You are urged to check beforehand to avoid inconvenience and surprises. Travel always involves a certain degree of risk, especially in low-cost areas. When travelling, especially on a budget, you should always take particular care to insure your safety.

INTRODUCTION

research when that planet was originally discovered and opened to commerce. There is no fear of such cultural traditions being encountered in the Klingon Empire, and safety can largely be guaranteed so long as the traveler visits Klingon worlds and colonies with a full understanding of the detailed traditions and beliefs of the people, particularly concerning honor and heritage.

The history of honor in the culture, and the depth of its importance to the modern Klingon society, is explored in all its fascinating detail. Fail to heed this lesson at your peril!

There is also information on Kiahz, a Klingon colony world where all the same rules apply as are found elsewhere in the Empire.

To understand what it means to be a Klingon is to understand where his world has been, what it has done and how it came together under a single planetary rule after living as a fragmentation of clans for so many centuries. The discovery of space flight went far in uniting the world, as the chapter on fleet organization makes evident.

The armistice between the Federation and the Empire is either easy or uneasy, depending on who is being interviewed. This book deepens an offworlder's understanding of what it means to be a Klingon, dispelling myths and approaching the heart of the truth. Just as there are many kinds of people in the Federation, so are there many kinds of people in the Klingon Empire.

FOCUS ON:

THE FOUNTAIN TREE: This tree grows on Quohl. It grows straight and tall, then branches out. The branches curve downward, thickly covered with small dangling leaves which dance in slight breezes, giving it a fountain-like appearance.

   In certain respects, Klingons can be better understood. They have a belief system and a bonding with ideas that is stronger than that found on most Federation worlds, and certainly more far-reaching than is any single cultural belief on Earth. The traveler who learns and understands this will find the Klingon Homeworld a place of vast richness and charm to be seen and experienced.

HOMEWORLD

QO'NOS: THE HOMEWORLD

by J.R. Bork

The Klingon homeworld is called by many names: Qo'noS, Klinzhai and YUQ (meaning "The World") are the most popular. The world has a KSC (Klingon Stellar Cartography) number and is identified by other races with different names and numbers.

What a Klingon means when he refers to his world depends largely on where he comes from and what dialog he speaks. Qo'noS is used for astrogation, much as Terra is used instead of Earth.

Qo'noS is the official name of the homeworld. Klinzhai is the name of the star around which Qo'noS orbits. It is also the name of one of the island nations on Qo'noS.

Many believe the history of the homeworld is only the history of the Empire. Despite the longevity of the Empire, this is hardly the truth. The first kingdom of Qo'noS was founded eight thousand years before the beginning of the Empire.

The first kingdom was known as the Valley of sSar. While much of life in that Kingdom is forgotten, it was the birthplace of many current Klingon rituals and customs. Klingon aversion to psychic powers began when the valley was under the rule of Ne'sahr, the Eater of Souls, a reputed magician of the first kingdom.

The Valley of sSar lasted six hundred years. Many great discoveries and inventions of the Klingon people began in the kingdom. Among these are the working of iron and the building of seaworthy vessels. The Valley provided the Klingon people with one of their most enduring legends. This was the birthplace of the legendary afterlife of the Black Fleet.

The fall of sSar is only legend. This period of history is known to Klingons as 'Iw poH, the Time of Blood.' It began approximately 7300 B.E. (before the founding of the Empire). It continued for almost four thousand years.

Few written records survive. It is believed the four thousand year long conflict began when warlords competed for power.

This long dark age shaped Klingon society. War became the Klingons natural state. Only the strongest and smartest families survived.

The remaining small townships could no longer mount full scale wars. They banded together in defense against roving bands of mounted warriors.

⚔ Foundation and Empire

The foremost town was built around the Korth Linehold. Korth reJ Kursa became Qorz, First King. The newly founded Kingdom of Qorz slaughtered, exiled or assimilated the remaining marauders.

One band founded a small kingdom of exiles. The Qayluur swore vengeance against Qorz. They eventually, many, many years later, played a small part in the fall of the Kingdom of Qorz.

The Kingdom of Qorz consolidated their position. Then they began to explore and conquer their world. They reached the peak of their power in 1490 B.E.

In that year the Kingdom of Qorz discovered the small island nation known as the Empire of Klinzhai. Its ruler was called Kol, Lord of Klinzhai and the Skies Above It. When the Qorzian explorers landed, they were met by Kol. He honored them with a feast and gave them gifts to bring to their king, Kaarth.

The suspicious explorers honored protocol and returned to Qorz with the gifts for their king. Kol meanwhile made plans to

---

FOCUS ON:

RED HOPPERS: These huge insects live in the plains of the temperate zone. They feast on grain. They plagued farmers until it was discovered they are repelled by a small native plant. The plant is now grown between rows of grain crops, eliminating the problem. When eaten, the insects offer high nutrition and are a staple of the diet of Klingons on Kiazh.

wrest his world from this false king.

Kaarth never got the chance to bestow appropriate gifts on Kol. Even as his explorers returned to their home port, Kol's war fleet was under sail. Kol himself never brought the war to Kaarth. His son, Kor, did. The war of Unification had begun.

The War of Unification raged for over six hundred hears. The ruling house of Qorz never understood that the war was fought on two fronts, on the battlefield and in the home.

The Empire allowed every family a voice. The dream of being part of a greater whole was brought to the Qorzian people. By the time of Molor, First King Twelfth, the Kingdom of Qorz had rotted from within. The people of Qorz were no longer loyal to their king.

⅃ Time of Blood

Only Molor's armies kept the people from rising against him. This control proved his downfall. When he tried to kill Kahless, Lord of Klinzhai and the Skies Above It, his own weapon was turned against him. Kuurus the Traitor brought the life of Molor, First King Twelfth, and of his oppressive kingdom to an end. On that day Kahless declared himself Emperor of the World and the Skies Above It.

The history of the Empire can be found in many history books. It is published in many languages, including Klingon and those of the Federation. Many stories are not in the official histories.

For an example, the histories bluntly state there has been no Emperor for the past three hundred years. The truth is that while there has been no acknowledged Emperor there have been many who proclaimed themselves as such.

Outsiders fail to understand Klingon ways. There are many Imperial families, but being born into such a bloodline does not make one heir to the throne. The Emperor's seat is won.

Sometimes winning comes hard, as in the case of Kagga, Emperor for a Day, whose crown was branded into his head. Sometimes it comes easy. Keth, the Centarian, ascended to the throne because none opposed him.

HOMEWORLD

For the last three hundred years, the Klingon Empire has suffered from a small scale "Time of Blood." Even the lowest level of power is fought for, won and defended.

History

One problem of Imperial History is that it occurs in triage. The Official State History is taught in schools to children and presented as the totality of Klingon history. There is the Line History kept by historians and embellished with the glory of that Line. Then there is the Oral History.

Tales often never saw print. They were memorized and retold as fables for all to hear. True traditionalists, Klingons preserved this tradition to the present. The story of the second Kahless' ascendancy is in the history books, but the tale is much more colorful than what appears.

To seek out the oral history of the Klingon Empire go to public festivals. Look for a Klingon with a large crowd around him. If the crowd is silent and his is the only voice, you will have found a teller of history. Listen and learn of things never printed in books.

A word of warning to non-Klingon historians: While most oral historians are frail and crippled with only large memories as their prowess, there is another side to this trade. Besides the Talkers of history, there are the Defenders of history. Should anything told by the Talkers be printed, the Defenders will remove the threat by any means. Very few survive their wrath.

To understand this is to begin to understand what it means to be Klingon.

KIAZH

Kiazh is one of many worlds conquered and settled by Klingons. It is the second planet in a five planet system.

The first planet in the system orbits too close to the sun. It is a burned out world. It keeps one side to the sun at all times, allowing a science post to exist on the dark side. The third planet is settled.

The fourth planet can be terraformed. A preparatory post has been established there. The fifth planet is a frozen waste.

Kiazh, the second planet, has been inhabited for many years. Humans first settled this world. Several colonies were developing the planet when it was discovered by the Klingon Empire.

When reports reached Qo'noS, he ordered that the world be taken. This was done with a minimum of destruction.

Humans who cooperated with occupation forces still serve their conquerors. The rest enrich its soil.

The planet has three continents. The largest, Klin-Kia, was the first settled. It supports the most people. It lies mostly in the temperate zone and offers a variety of terrain, ranging from mountains to plains to valleys. Its largest city is Kiaza.

Topography

Zhaik is largely mountainous, with flatlands on the coasts. Volcanoes dot the continent, which lies mostly in the southern hemisphere. Jungles border the mountains.

A few cities lie along the coasts. Mining is conducted along with the harvesting of tropical fruits and woods.

Quohl straddles the equator. It is covered with thick jungle. One mountain chain cuts through the center from north to south. Prosperous cities exploit the jungles and house industry and export companies.

Large and small islands lie in the world's vast oceans. The south pole is an ice cap while the north pole has a small ice-covered continent with several science stations.

KIAZH

Kiazh is one of many worlds conquered and settled by Klingons. It is the second planet in a five planet system.

The first planet in the system orbits too close to the sun. It is a burned out world. It keeps one side to the sun at all times, allowing a science post to exist on the dark side. The third planet is settled.

The fourth planet can be terraformed. A preparatory post has been established there. The fifth planet is a frozen waste.

Kiazh, the second planet, has been inhabited for many years. Humans first settled this world. Several colonies were developing the planet when it was discovered by the Klingon Empire.

When reports reached Qo'noS, he ordered that the world be taken. This was done with a minimum of destruction.

Humans who cooperated with occupation forces still serve their conquerors. The rest enrich its soil.

The planet has three continents. The largest, Klin-Kia, was the first settled. It supports the most people. It lies mostly in the temperate zone and offers a variety of terrain, ranging from mountains to plains to valleys. Its largest city is Kiaza.

Topography

Zhaik is largely mountainous, with flatlands on the coasts. Volcanoes dot the continent, which lies mostly in the southern hemisphere. Jungles border the mountains.

A few cities lie along the coasts. Mining is conducted along with the harvesting of tropical fruits and woods.

Quohl straddles the equator. It is covered with thick jungle. One mountain chain cuts through the center from north to south. Prosperous cities exploit the jungles and house industry and export companies.

Large and small islands lie in the world's vast oceans. The south pole is an ice cap while the north pole has a small ice-covered continent with several science stations.

Flora

The native vegetation of Kiazh includes many bizarre growths.

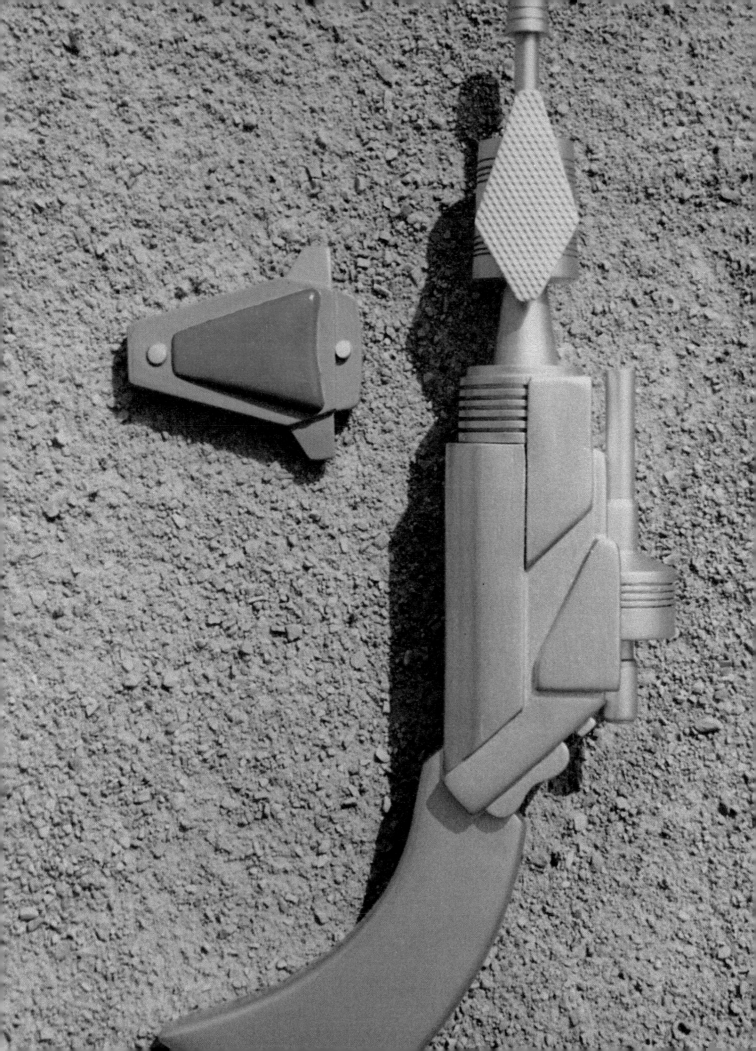

THE **TORAD TREE** has a twisted trunk and long, slender pointed leaves. Its wood has a peculiar grain of swirled and grooved patterns. It is prized for decorative items. The trees are found on Zhaik.

THE **FOUNTAIN TREE** grows on Quohl. It grows straight and tall, then branches out. The branches curve downward, thickly covered with small dangling leaves which dance in slight breezes, giving it a fountain-like appearance.

PIGMY TREES are found on the fringes of forests and jungles. They grow slightly taller than a man. Some grow even smaller. Size is determined by the amount of rainfall during their first year of growth.

THE **CELERY TREE** resembles a stalk of celery, a vegetable eaten on Terra. Multiple ridged trunks rise straight and tall, then divide to form branches of lacy yellow-green leaves which give off a celery-like odor. Young buds and leaves are edible.

THE POPNUT TREE offers an interesting phenomenon. It is roughly the size of a Terran cherry tree, with black wood and greenish black leaves. Its crown is flat with many branches, somewhat like the African Acacia tree on Terra or the Blackcrown of Klinzhai. It bears pale yellow blossoms in spring that develop into fist-sized nuts in autumn. When they are fully ripe, the pods spring open with a popping sound, and nuts fall to the ground. The delicious nuts are exported.

THE RAINBOW TREE is cultivated for its beauty and aroma. As the tree matures, it changes color from pale yellow to bright yellow then green, and, finally, blue. Very old trees are deep blue. In spring leaves are a light hue, deepening as the season progresses. In fall, all leaves turn black and rapidly disintegrate into the soil.

Other exotic plants and flowers grow in the jungles and forests. There are many thick, fleshy, man-eating varieties. Some plants have tentacles with suction cups; others exude a euphoric perfume to lure prey. Some even shoot stun-needles at those who venture into the forests.

THE TENTACLE PLANT resembles a water lily. It is blue-green in color with a cup shaped form. When an animal wanders near, long, slender bright yellow tentacles covered with sticky sap reach out to seize it and draw it in.

Large, beautiful and complex blooms decorate many jungle plants. The huge, spotted orange PARASOL PLANT hangs downward in the dark and dim light. It lifts its cup during the day. The equally large purple THISTLE-BALL bears its blooms on slender stalks that rise from the heart of the plant.

THE MOTION PLANT is one of several varieties that open and close their blooms several times a minute. Larger than the others, it stands taller than a man. The long petals of its white flowers unfold, showing red-streaked inner petals, yellow stamens and an orange pistil. Then the long petals close again. The plant is self-pollinating.

THE MILK-PLANT was discovered in the valleys of the south temperate zone of Kiazh shortly after settlers arrived. It is has been domesticated for its highly nutritious milk. The milk is found in its fleshy stems and leaves, as well as its roots. The milk is pressed out, then diluted with water. Native animals relish it.

Fauna

Animal life on Kiazh is as exotic as the flora. Strange creatures include the stick-limbed money-lizard, the high springing red hoppers and the waddling mud-birds.

MONKEY-LIZARDS inhabit the tropical jungles of Kiazh. They possess snake-like scales in multicolored patterns. They resemble monkeys and agilely leap between tree branches, emitting almost continuous hissing sounds. They feed on flowers, fruit and insects.

RED HOPPERS   These huge insects live in the plains of the temperate zone. They feast on grain. They plagued farmers until it was discovered they are repelled by a small native plant. The plant is now grown between rows of grain crops, eliminating the problem. When eaten, the insects offer high nutrition and are a staple of the diet of Klingons on Kiazh.

THE SLIME SLUG   One of many edible insects, the living bug is eaten. When chilled they taste similar to vanilla, but much stronger. The bugs are used to garnish cold desserts. Their slow movement offers an artistic effect to the dish.

THE CRISP BEETLE   is used to garnish meats. It has a spicy, peppery flavor. Lightly toast before sprinkling on servings.

A segmented worm called the KHOK is used in salads. It adds a lemony flavor when eaten alive.

Kiazh offers much to visitors, both Klingon and non-Klingon alike. The armistice that brought the Klingons into the Federation allows humans to come and go as they please. Humans have established a new colony on Kiazh. Klingons protect the colony along with their own long-established townships.

KLINGON CULTURE AND NIGHT LIFE

by J.R. Bork

Nightlife in the Klingon Empire is varied and plentiful. Klingons engage in many nocturnal activities. Drinking, eating, and dancing establishments thrive in every major city. An unaccompanied tourist must exercise caution and not venture far from the tourist sections of the cities.

A Klingon companion will open many doors. Travelers must still be wary. Visitors, particularly humans, are new to the Klingons. The following guide tells the adventuresome traveler of unforeseen pleasures and unspeakable hazards on the homeworld.

Drinking Etiquette

Klingons like to drink. They offer a wide range of selections in their bars. Tourists usually drink in the safety of their hotels. Few other places will allow tourists entry on their own.

Drinking establishments serve drinks from throughout the galaxy. Until recently public houses did not exist on the homeworld. While Klingons as a people have sworn off drinking, many still imbibe.

In the past alcohol was often a tool of assassination. The unsuspecting victim died quickly after downing a poison laden drink. The problem was eliminated by private houses.

Large groups of Klingons drink in these places. Guests bring their own liquor and are served by lineless bartenders.

As poison fell into disuse, the bartenders began stocking alcohol. Eventually private houses became public houses. Terrans call them pubs.

Many pubs still hold private stocks of liqueur for regular customers. It is a great honor to be asked to share drinks from someone's private stock. Refusing this honor is often fatal. If you believe the person honoring you would serve you poison, you do not belong on the homeworld.

Along with imports, Klingon pubs serve a wide variety of interesting Klingon drinks. Terrans are familiar with one of the most popular:

Chocolate. Sugar produces a mild euphoria in Klingons. Drinks containing sugar are intoxicating to Klingons.

Chocolate, originally imported from the Federation, is now a major Klingon crop. Drinks made from native chocolates are richer than imported ones. The most popular is *Hegh yuch,* also known as chocolate death. This drink is so strong it produces mild euphoria in almost any race that drinks it.

⅃ Klingon Drinks

BLOODWINE   Do not confuse this drink with Regullan Blood Wine. Klingon blood wine is fermented from the roots of the Tso plant.

The Tso plant drinks no water. It leeches blood from passing animals and Klingons. Klingon bloodwine contains blood. The strong wine tastes sweet, with a slightly metallic aftertaste. Color depends on the region of origin. It can range from blood purple to transparent pink in color. This drink should not be missed.

BLACK ALES   There are several commercially available black ales. Black ales should be served warm or piping hot. The syrup of *gfai* beans is fermented with grains to create the black drink. The syrup carbonates the liquid. The ales taste bitter on the tongue, but deliver an extraordinarily sweet aftertaste. Commercial varieties are the dregs of the cask mixed with black colored water. They don't taste the same as a private stock. If you cannot avail yourself of a private stock do taste a public one.

KLINGON SALT WATER   Most races should drink a chaser with Klingon salt water. The drink is made of sea salt and tuber alcohol. The salty drink is very strong, approaching 200 proof. Without a sweet, syrupy chaser, most races will choke on this Klingon delicacy. It is highly recommended.

KLINGON GREEN DRAGON   This drink is no longer made. Several thousand five hundred gallon casks remain on the home-world. The origins of this drink are unknown. In its pure state it also makes a good solvent.

Drinkers of pure Green Dragon often remark that it numbs the lips and tongue. Partakers often fail to notice how much this drink burns their esophagi and stomachs. It must only be drunk in diluted form. A twelve-to-one ratio renders it safe. The drink offers an unforgettable experience.

Many offworlders are pleased that Klingon pubs never close. Klingon pubs lack windows. Proprietors allow customers to buy drinks on credit. Many tourists spend much more than they intend. When the barkeep finally says, "Pay now," he can be quite insistent. Enjoy your drinking, but keep track of what you are spending.

◢ Klingon Foods

Tourists often believe Klingons eat all their food alive and raw. This is not true. While many foods are best left in their *natural* state, many must be cooked. Some foods are not normally available to tourists.

ZENTAUR HAUNCH The meat is similar to lamb and not native to Klingon. The Zentaur, or Zentari, as they call themselves, are considered sentient beings within the Federation. Eating Zentaur is a crime for Federation citizens.

The meat is cooked with the leaves and roots of the Toragh plant. The leaves dissolve into a fine sauce. The roots are served on the side.

WHITEFANG STEAK The pungent, tender meat comes from a canine-like animal. Whitefang is served with the outside seared and a very rare center. It is served with various sauces. The dish is accompanied by traqs, small, sweet-tasting, slug-like creatures. Traqs are served live but can be killed for the squeamish. This highly recommended dish is only available in the winter.

BOILED TARGSHEAD SOUP   Most tourists are familiar with targs. This soup is a festival dish. It is served at Consortship Ceremonies, Rites of Inclusion and Ascension Anniversaries. Fortunately for tourists, these events are daily occurrences. Unfortunately they are private festivals. A visitor must be accompanied by a Klingon.

The targs head is thrown into a vat of boiling oil. It is cooked until the meat is reduced to a liquid. It is then removed from the fire. Several root vegetables are thrown in. After cooling, it is passed around in a large bowl. Each celebrant drinks as much as he can. This dish highly recommended.

QIRTS   This fish lives around a large volcanic vent in the ocean off the coast of the Broken Land. They are found in no other location. They swim in circles around the vent sucking in abundant microscopic life. Once a Qirts begins to circle, it always swims in one direction. One side of its body atrophies while the other grows muscular.

As qirts age, they swim closer to the vent. Eventually they use two tailfin tendrils to anchor themselves to the vent's edge. Within days they are dead, and fully cooked.

Qirts are harvested when the cooked fishes float to the top. This dish is hard to find outside the Broken Land. Several restaurants in Throne City import it and charge exorbitant prices. To sample this dish, go to Qortazh on the Street of Warriors. He's the only one who leaves the tendrils on; the tendrils are the best part.

FOCUS ON:

THE MOTION PLANT: This is one of several varieties that open and close their blooms several times a minute. Larger than the others, it stands taller than a man. The long petals of its white flowers unfold, showing red-streaked inner petals, yellow stamens and an orange pistil. Then the long petals close again. The plant is self-pollinating.

STUFFED FIREBLOSSOM BOWLS   Offworlders are shocked to learn Klingons eat a variety of plant life. They are largely used as garnishes on a meat dish. Many tourists buy fireblossoms to cultivate in their own gardens. Unfortunately they soon learn that fireblossoms kill other plants.

Klingons plant them separate from other plants. The gardens produce large fireblossom bulbs. They are stuffed with larval gagh and set ablaze. When they stop burning, an excellent meal is ready for the knowledgeable consumer.

Ⴢ Foods to Avoid

Tourists must avoid these foods. Most are poisonous. Others are deadly if not prepared properly.

BEETLH   Avoid any dish with this ingredient. Beetlh is a virtually indestructible Klingon pet. They are eaten when they die. Beetlh die when their bodies fill with spawn.

Dead adult Beetlh are eaten by passing scavengers. Eating them is fatal. Beetlh spawn gestate in the stomach of the unwary scavenger. When gestation is complete, the infant Beetlh eat their way out of the host. One runs the risk of being eaten by one's dinner.

BLUE VEGETABLES   The blue color of these vegetables comes from cyanide in the cellulose structure of the plants. These vegetables are poisonous to many species. Klingon tea is made from a blue plant. Many races drink an antidote with it.

SPINY GAGH   This warning is only for Vulcanoids. Spiny gagh are not true gagh. These crustaceans live in the northern seas of the Homeworld. The young are larger than adults. Adults secrete a poison that causes their young's copper-based blood to congeal momentarily. This is not fatal for spiny gagh. It is fatal for Vulcanoids.

'RROTMEY   These mall fried grubs look like brown spheres. They are difficult for tourists to avoid. The suffix "-mey" in their name means "scattered all about." The finger foods are served at any Klingon gathering.

The delicious food is the nearest Klingon equivalent to Terran "popcorn." Much of their flavor comes from acid. The acid produces a pleasant, warm feeling in Klingons. It burns a hole through the stomach lining of non-Klingons. While not immediately fatal, 'rrotmey cause great pain. Unless medical attention is immediate, a handful of Klingon "popcorn" will be the last thing you eat.

Restaurant Etiquette

Be certain of the contents of your meal. Simply ask your server. Most restaurateurs will be pleased to inform you whether your food will kill you. You may not want to eat at the exceptions.

There are many restaurants on the homeworld. Most restaurants give offworlders an abridged menu. Upon receiving a tourist menu, look at your server and say, "jilegh nuqdaq 'oH Qe'QoQ'e'." Then stand, as if to leave. Your server will look at you with new respect, ask you to wait and promptly bring you a proper Klingon menu.

Night Life

There is more to Klingon night life than eating and drinking. Movies, theater and *Tera'nganhol*, or music clubs, abound.

Moviegoers must understand Klingon ways. Theater is diverse. Most popular is "Klingon Opera." The stories told in semi-musical form vary from tales of great battles to Line histories to morality plays. They can be grandiose or humble.

Every tourist should see Shakespeare translated into this format. Klingons insist the great bard originally wrote in Klingonese. Romeo and Juliet take on whole new life when one understands the Line war between the K'puleth and the mon'tagu.'

Klingon music stuns most visitors. Classical styles are often played on instruments that sound like battlefield agonies or war cries of blood-crazed combatants.

The inspirational music wraps the listener in sound, pulling them to ever greater heights of glory. Dances accompanying this music are often intricate forms of ritualized battle. Moves and counter-moves are made with the seeming intent of defeating a partner.

Like most older forms of dance, subtle moves of Klingon classical dancing are difficult for tourists to learn. A few forms are simple enough for anyone with a slight sense of rhythm, and a desire to learn.

The most popular classical dance was originally called "The Struggle Dance." It was renamed, by offworlders. They dubbed it "The Klingon Waltz."

It has become popular offworld because it does not mandate relative positions of dancers. Dancers must only clasp hands with their fingers interlaced while the leader takes three steps forward, one step to the left then three steps back, and finally a step to the right bringing him to his original position. Then the leader begins again.

There are no stated flourishes. Dancers invent their own. The dance takes new shapes with the flow of the music, the emotions of the dancers and the size of the crowd.

♪ Overload

Klingon "popular" music is rougher, louder and faster than that of most worlds. It is usually performed by groups of intoxicated musicians. It slows then grows louder and faster until the musicians get tired and stop. The music mangles the senses, giving it its most popular name, "Overload."

Dancing accompanying this music is a stylized form of ritual combat. Terran historians liken it to an antiquated form of home-world dancing known as "Slam Dancing."

Offworlders who wish to try this dance should scan the historical records of Terra then apply the ideas to Klingons. It is not danger ous. One objective is to get in and out without getting hit. There is little danger as dancers are unarmed.

Those who choose to watch but not participate should remain wary. The center of the dance moves. Unwary observers are often caught in the middle.

♪ Male/Female Relations

Every gender and species will be attracted to some Klingon. The Empire contains many different peoples. Few *ask* to join. Fewer still enjoy the status of citizens. It is common to witness Klingon warriors strolling arm-in-arm with green Orions, Caitians or even humans.

You could inadvertently become part of a Klingon courtship. Intent is usually stated at formal events. It can be accepted or declined.

Things can be less clear in drinking houses and back streets. It is often said that humans are too fragile for Klingons. This is not true.

Males must be wary. Packs of drunken Klingon females are easily aroused. They will literally love a male to death. Only the luckiest beings survive; they may be taken as consorts.

If you get into the previously described situation, all we can say is, "batlh Daqowlu'taH."

♪ Small Talk and Body Language

BUYING DRINKS Buying drinks is a common human custom. It is indulged on many worlds of the Federation. The custom is not observed by Klingons.

Klingons do not give to one another freely, except under very special circumstances, or at certain times of the year. At any other time, such action invokes the tradition of "gift protocol."

The protocol declares that if one gives something to another, the gift-giver will soon come to claim their own gift. Between members of the opposite sex, the intent is clear. The action declares: "I am coming to get you."

This is not a wise action for a human. If you buy a drink for a Klingon it states the value you place on them. Most Klingons are highly insulted by this gesture. Many duels result from this matter of honor.

FLIRTING Klingons sometimes bypass the need for conversation. This is usually initiated by females, and directed at someone the female knows is interested. Klingons normally engage in familiar flirtations similar to those of other species.

Offworlders who overhear Klingon small talk are often shocked. While apparent behavior is similar, the underlying culture is markedly different. To understand this it is necessary to understand the mating habits of Klingons.

Klingons are a race of conquerors. Those conquered are not considered equals. Klingons engaged in small talk are trying to determine status. For Klingons the battle of the sexes is literal. The battle never ends. Klingons find joy in battle.

Klingon courting frightens offworlders. Intimate conversation sounds like a heated argument about to erupt into violence. It is.

The culture is based on war. Mating is defined in military terms. Offworlders insulted by an attractive Klingon of the opposite sex should not apologize.

This will lessen their value. The hoped for sexual encounter may still take place, but under very different terms. The offworlder will cease to be the conqueror and become the conquered. They may not be allowed to leave.

Instead, the offworlder should reply to the insult by the Klingon in kind. The insults must be flirtatious and must not criticize honor, family or Empire. The responses must be quick and direct.

The process is continuous. If verbal responses are right, action will erupt. Then it starts over without words.

This is but the tip of the glacier of Klingon night life. Nothing has been said of the many public festivals and celebrations that fill the Klingon year. These are covered in most guide books. This book also says nothing about rural customs or the night life of Imperial worlds. It focuses only on the homeworld.

HONOR

KLINGON CODE OF HONOR

by Steven J. Frey

Non-Klingons understand that honor is part of Klingon culture. Most are unaware Klingon society places honor above all else.

A Klingon, particularly a warrior, values honor more than family, career or life. A Klingon warrior's greatest wish is to die in battle with honor. It is believed the honored dead join Kahless the Unforgettable in Sto-Vo-Kor, a Klingon variation of the Christian's Heaven.

Klingons who die without honor are believed doomed to spend eternity in Gre'thor, analogous to Terrans's Hell. It is guarded by a half Klingon, half beast called Fek'lhr. Warriors bringing great glory to the Empire are awarded the Medallion of Kahless. Recipients of the medallion never boast of their accomplishment or display the medallion in public.

An individual can bring honor or dishonor to his family. Children are taught honor at an early age. They become responsible for the actions of their forebears and can pass honor or dishonor to their offspring.

The head of a family shares his reputation with the entire family, including siblings and their descendants. Family honor may be regained by killing the shamed individual or absolution from the current leader of the Klingon Empire.

At the beginning of this century, the belief in "honor above all else" did not exist. Honor was considered a despicable trait. Encountering treacherous, deceitful Klingons led Starfleet to adopt a policy of covert surveillance before first contact.

During this century, observers note a change in Klingon attitude regarding honor. The warrior Maltz first demonstrated modern Klingon honor. He was deceived by a Starfleet officer and transported a landing party onto his own ship. The Starfleet personnel threatened to kill him if he would not cooperate. Upon realizing the severity of his mistake, Maltz stated, "I do not deserve to live," and insisted on being executed.

HONOR

⟫ The End of Honor

This shift in attitude is a topic of debate within the Federation. The Intelligence and Diplomatic Corps correlate the changes in public opinion with changes in Klingon government.

Klingon sacred scrolls state that Kahless was the greatest warrior who ever lived. He united his people by killing the tyrant, Molor. Afterward he gave his hand forged sword the name, bat'telh, the sword of honor. It is believed the name was taken from the city, Kling. It is said to be the place Kahless defeated Molor.

Empire Union Day is celebrated once a year to commemorate Kahless's installation as Emperor. The stories of Kahless were passed on from generation to generation. The legends grew into parables.

One such story tells how Kahless fought his brother, Morath, for twelve days and twelve nights. Morath had brought dishonor to his family by telling a lie. Tales of Kahless provide examples for the Klingon people, setting the pattern of conquests and the code of proper conduct.

The last Emperor died in 2058 with no apparent heirs. The Klingon people chose a new leader. They allowed challengers to demonstrate honor and worthiness in battle to the death.

After defeating all opponents, K'vak claimed the title of Chancellor. He declared himself supreme ruler of the Klingon Empire. This event marked the beginning of the waning of honor within Klingon society.

Startling new research of this document may reveal a massive cover-up immediately following K'vak's coronation. Accusations of illegal acts were never proven due to disappearances and "accidental" deaths of witnesses.

FOCUS ON:

BLUE VEGETABLES: The blue color of these vegetables comes from cyanide in the cellulose structure of the plants. These vegetables are poisonous to many species. Klingon tea is made from a blue plant. Many races drink an antidote with it.

The Klingon people needed a strong leader to guide them. K'vak demonstrated the benefits and profitability of a subversive lifestyle. Honor and loyalty were replaced by greed and deceit. Mistrust and paranoia spread throughout the Empire and lasted several generations.

♪ A Deceitful Nature

Klingons and humans fought since their initial meeting in 2218. Klingons demonstrated treachery, deceit and dishonor.

Starfleet records that on Stardate 3198.4 Captain James T. Kirk of the starship Enterprise encountered Commander Kor of the Klingon occupation army. After meeting resistance from Kirk and his first officer, Kor ordered the execution of two hundred Organian hostages.

It is noteworthy that modern Klingons do not take hostages. It is considered a cowardly act, not befitting an honorable man.

Kirk subdued a Klingon soldier who saved his own life by revealing vital information. This conflicts with Maltz's belief in "death before dishonor."

Kirk failed to defeat Kor because he didn't know Klingon operating procedure. Kor stated, "Do you know why we are so strong? Because we are a unit, each of us is part of the greater whole, always under surveillance, even a Commander such as myself. Always under surveillance."

As always, an honorable man can be trusted. A dishonorable man must be monitored at all times.

The Klingon agent Kras also demonstrated deceit. While working to secure a mining treaty, Kras broke his word. He concealed a focused energy weapon. The scrupulously honest Capellans killed him for it.

The greatest example of Klingon treachery occurred on Deep Space Station K-7. It involved the dispute over Sherman's planet.

Arne Darvin, assistant to Federation Undersecretary of Agricultural Affairs Nilz Barris, poisoned a shipment of quadrotriticale. Barris was discovered to be a Klingon spy. He could have been responsible for the deaths of thousands of innocents he never faced in battle. Modern Klingons would never kill in such a fashion.

⏿ Back to Honor

Change began when Gorkon's father, Korax, was dying from old age. The young politician was poised to become head of his family. On his death bed, Korax stated, "This is not the way a warrior should die."

Gorkon was puzzled. He asked his father to explain. Korax told of ancient beliefs, of how warriors die in battle with honor.

Honor was new to Gorkon. He dismissed it as the ramblings of a dying, old man. After his father died, Gorkon discovered the teachings of Kahless hidden among his father's possessions. The words profoundly moved him. They inspired him to dedicating his life to returning his people to the ways of the past.

He took becoming Chancellor and restoring honor to the Klingon Empire as his top priorities. Gorkon rose through the political ranks. When he became Chancellor, he rewarded honor with appointment to the High Council.

The Empire soon divided. One faction supported Gorkon's restoration of the honorable ways of old. The other clung to treachery as a way of life.

The explosion of the Klingon moon, Praxis, gave Gorkon the opportunity to settle the issue. He formed an alliance with the Federation to create what he called, "a brave new world."

Those unwilling to change conspired against Gorkon. They killed him and attempted to kill his successor, his daughter Azetbur. A horrified Klingon people returned to the ways of old.

The loss of so noble and honest a man shocked them. It demonstrated the ugliness of subversion. They found no glory in defeating an enemy without honest combat.

After the Camp Khitomer peace conference in 2293, Azetbur restructured the Klingon High Council. She replaced all councilors opposed to returning the Empire to the ways of honor with members of the strongest and most honorable families. Azetbur rewarded

HONOR

honor and banished dishonorable men from society.

◢ The Value of Honor

Subsequent leaders of the High Council preserved ancient, honorable beliefs. K'mpec presided over the Council longer than any other. The strong leader instilled the value of honor in his people.

When evidence surfaced against Ja'rod, father of council member Duras, K'mpec quickly resolved the matter. Ja'rod had conspired with the Romulans in 2346, resulting in the Khitomer massacre. Duras was the head of a powerful family. Public recognition of the treason would have torn the Empire apart.

K'mpec chose to blame Mogh, a dead victim of the massacre. When two surviving sons of Mogh were discovered, K'mpec persuaded the eldest to accept decommendation to save the Empire.

K'mpec maintained stability in the Empire until Duras poisoned him. Then K'mpec boldly named Jean-Luc Picard, a non-Klingon, Arbiter of Succession. Picard insisted on the ja'chug (succession process).

Duras and his rival, political newcomer Gowron, were required to prove their worthiness. They had to declare all their victories and all the glory they brought to the Klingon Empire.

During this selection process, Duras murdered K'Ehleyr, the Federation's ambassador to K'mpec. She had discovered evidence of the cover-up of the Khitomer massacre. Claiming the right of vengeance, Mogh's eldest son, Worf, killed Duras. K'Ehleyr had been Worf's mate. With no other challengers, Picard named Gowron leader of the High Council.

The Duras family then conspired with the Romulans to place Toral, an illegitimate son of Duras, in political power. The involvement of the Romulans plunged the Klingon Empire into civil war.

The sons of Mogh, Worf and Kurn, offered their support to Gowron in exchange for the restoration of their family honor. Worf's friends in the Federation, and three Klingon squadrons under the command of Kurn, proved too powerful for Duras and the

HONOR

Romulans. Gowron kept his promise and restored honor to the Mogh family name.

⏾ The Return of Kahless

Gowron was a strong military and political leader. He could not lead his people in the ways of the spirit. The honorable man needed a guide for his people.

The civil war had destroyed belief in honor. Corruption and dishonor threatened the Empire. Recognizing the need for moral leadership, the high clerics of Boreth produced a clone from the original Kahless. They imprinted the clone's synaptic pathways with the memories of Kahless as written in the sacred scrolls.

News of Kahless's return traveled quickly throughout the Empire. It sparked new hope. Gowron challenged the pretender to his crown. He discovered the truth and wanted the clone and the clerics of Boreth executed.

Gowron became convinced that the execution would plunge the Empire into civil war. He conceded that the clone was the rightful heir to the throne of Kahless. A symbol of honor and stability, Kahless assumed the role as ceremonial Emperor of the Klingon people. He returned them to the ways of honor.

Advances in cloning technology guarantee the Klingon people will have Kahless as their spiritual leader for many centuries. Support for his leadership is not certain. As different families rise to power within the Empire, public opinion may change.

Intergalactic travelers should learn the traditions and customs of a planet and its inhabitants before visiting. The Klingon home world is no exception.

Questioning or insulting Klingon honor is met with a sharp blade to the throat. Many intergalactic traders have lost their lives due to hasty words. If public opinion again changes, only a fool will trust a Klingon to keep his word. For now a majority of Klingons will die to prevent that from ever coming to pass again.

RELIGION

THE ROLE OF KAHLESS IN KLINGON RELIGION

by Trey Causey

The unifying belief among Klingons for more than a thousand years has been reverence for Kahless. Modern Klingons benefit from his enduring wisdom.

Human students find Klingon religion and mythology puzzling. It lacks "deities." Archeological evidence indicates the practice of animism among Paleolithic Klingons. This never evolved into the anthropomorphic forms found in most Terran religions.

Some suggest this stems from Klingon refusal to recognize power greater than their own. This peculiarity leads uninformed writers to state that Klingons have no religion. Nothing could be further from the truth.

The Klingon Empire encompasses many worlds, cultures and belief systems. The fundamental mythic cycle of the race that founded the Empire is that of Kahless the Unforgettable. Kahless combines the characteristics of many figures in Terran history/mythology, including Moses, Odin, Hercules, and Gilgamesh, with a few messianic attributes thrown in.

The Kahless legend is based on a real person born into a nomadic Klingon tribe a little over 1500 years ago. This was during the 9th century AD on Earth. His early life remains shrouded in mystery.

There are no commonly accepted legends of this period of his life. Kahless may have distinguished himself early in life. His culture valued strength and skill with weapons.

Kahless rose to be chieftain of his tribe. Other tribes also fell under Kahless' rule. Within a few years Kahless became the acknowledged leader of all nomadic tribes in the area. He built a large army to conquer Kling, the capital city of the Emperor Molor.

Kahless is credited with uniting the Klingon city-states into the Empire. Actually Molor began this work while Kahless was still a boy. When Kahless marched his armies to Kling, Molor ruled an empire of 28 city-states.

55

Molor is immortalized as the greatest tyrant in Klingon history. Molor may have been cruel and ruthless, even by Klingon standards. Legend tells that countless warriors challenged him to free their city from his rule, but none could defeat him. The coming of Kahless would change that.

The Fall of Molor

Kahless encamped his army at the Lake of Lursor. There he fashioned a bat'telh. Tradition states this was the first ever made. It was formed from a lock of his own hair.

Actually the bat'telh was in use among the nomads for many years but was unknown outside their lands. Armed with his new bat'telh, Kahless and his forces marched toward the city. Kahless stood at Kling's great walls and demanded that Molor meet him in personal combat. Molor agreed. Kahless defeated and killed the tyrant.

Under other circumstances the nomads would have been viewed as invaders. The cities would have repulsed them. Molor was so hated that the city dwellers welcomed the nomads as saviors. According to legend, they immediately declared Kahless their new emperor.

The truth of these matters lies shrouded in the mists of history.

FOCUS ON:

BEETLH: Avoid any dish with beetlh as an ingredient. Beetlh is a virtually indestructible Klingon pet. They are eaten when they die. Beetlh die when their bodies fill with spawn.

Dead adult Beetlh are eaten by passing scavengers. Eating them is fatal. Beetlh spawn gestate in the stomach of the unwary scavenger. When gestation is complete, the infant Beetlh eat their way out of the host. One runs the risk of being eaten by one's dinner.

It is only known that Kahless became emperor with little destruction or bloodshed. The nomads abandoned their former lifestyle settling into the cities as a new nobility. The tribes eventually evolved into the Great Houses of the Klingon Empire. The tribal council that advised Kahless became the Great Council.

Perhaps inspired by Molor, Kahless set out to build an empire governed from Kling. Decades of war and diplomacy brought success to Kahless where Molor had failed. All of Qo'noS grew united under his empire, the Klingon Empire.

Throughout his world, Klingons spoke of him as "Kahless, who will not be forgotten." Kahless the barbarian had become the first emperor. The greatest figure in Klingon mythology would be remembered as Kahless the Unforgettable. His empire grew outward to the stars.

♪ Legendary Kahless

The legend of Kahless outgrew the man. It assumed many roles in Klingon culture. Kahless appears as purveyor of wisdom and establisher of social conduct. He appears as hero and warrior without peer. He also appears as a messiah.

Kahless, like the Norse god, Odin, appears in many tales, providing small bits of wisdom. A good example is the tale of the Man of Quin'lat.

A great storm strikes the city during a visit by Kahless. One mighty warrior of the city claims he will go out into the storm, stating, "I will stand before the wind and make it respect me." The high winds dash the man against the walls of the city and kill him. Kahless, who had watched the whole drama passively then comments, "The wind does not respect a fool."

The tales of Kahless instill the virtues important to the Klingon people. The most famous Kahless story tells of his battle with Morath, his oft-erring brother. Morath tells a lie, reflecting badly on his family. In the lie Kahless appears a coward.

Kahless challenges Morath to fight. Morath refuses and runs away. Kahless chases him a great distance. Kahless finally catches him and they wrestle for twelve days and twelve nights. In the end Morath was suitably chastised for his wrong doing.

Kahless' most often appears as warrior hero. He is the Klingon Hercules. He slays the tyrant giant Molor after a titanic battle. He drops a lock of his hair into the lava in the Kris'tak Volcano, cools it in the Lake of Lursor, then twists it in his bare hands into the first bat'telh. In other legends he wrestles with demons and banishes them from the world, or kills monsters threatening his empire. In death, he waits in Sto-Vo-Kor, the Klingon Valhalla, where he greets the honored dead who come to fight glorious battles for all eternity.

⅃ The Legends

Some of these stories clearly did not originate with Kahless. They were deeds of other heroes eventually absorbed into the Kahless myth. The story of Kahless' defeat of demons can be traced to the homeworld's southern continent. It began as a tale of a hero named Ngarakkani. Kahless' battle with the great monster Krek'atlh was originally attributed to Quin'lat's patron hero, Durgath.

The most important aspect of Kahless is his role as messiah. "The Story of Promise" says that after he united the Klingon home-world, Kahless proclaimed it time for him to leave his people. The people cried and begged him not to leave them. Kahless only said he must go ahead to Sto-Vo-Kor and prepare it for all the valiant war-riors who would return one day to lead his people. He pointed to a star in the sky and said his people should look for him there, "on that point of light." Kahless then disappeared into the wilderness, never to be seen again.

Monasteries arose to preserve the tomes containing the lore of Kahless. The clerics told the tales of Kahless to Klingon children. While the role of clerics varied from city to city, all maintained the traditions and held fast to their belief in the Story of Promise.

When the Klingon empire expanded to the stars, the clerics established a monastery on a planet orbiting the star Kahless pointed to in legend. They named the planet Boreth. It now houses many Klingon relics.

The nature of these relics is not recorded. Clerics refuse to let Federation scholars view them. Boreth is a historical treasure throve.

ꓓ Kahless Now

Scholars of the Kahless legend note that the story has not changed over the past 1000 years. No new characters were added. No lesser figures took their place beside Kahless as Gawain and Lancelot stood beside Arthur.

There are a host of regional Klingon heroes. No others besides Kahless are universally accepted by all Klingons.

Kahless has not been elevated to a deity. Even to his clerics, Kahless is the messiah, but he is not a god. This is an important distinction that separates Klingon religious thought from that of many other cultures.

A full discussion of the social and religious importance of the Kahless legends on the formation and development of the Klingon Empire would fill several lengthy volumes.

Klingons have written whole libraries on the topic. Federation scholars diligently work to catch up. Kahless the Unforgettable is an integral part of the Klingon Empire.

Knowledge of Kahless is woefully incomplete. Little Klingon scholarly work has been devoted to the archaeological and historical investigation of the truth behind the stories. The Klingons have not allowed Federation scholars access to important sites. Klingons prefer the legends to the truth.

It is hoped that this brief essay provides the reader with a small insight into the Kahless mythos. The goal is explain major misconceptions about the Klingon belief system. Others have delved more deeply into this fascinating topic.

I encourage readers to seek out the numerous works on the subject. They discuss the topic at greater length than is possible here. Many of these works are available direct from public library databases.

DUELING

THE DUELING TRADITION

by Ann K. Schwader

One colorful but little understood aspect of Klingon society is the tradition of the personal duel. The tradition serves vital needs of the Empire. Visitors must familiarize themselves with the fundamentals of the tradition. Such familiarity enhances appreciation of Klingon folkways, and avoids potentially lethal misunderstandings.

A Social Tradition

Dueling helps maintain unique cultural values. The right to a duel circle confirms a Klingon warrior's identity. It links him to a glorious past.

Most UFP citizens find blood duels disgusting and barbaric. It keeps Feds at arm's length. Dueling serves notice that the Empire, though now allied with the UFP, does not share the Federation's pacifist mores. While Federation citizens bleat that "we may be killers, but we won't kill today," the Klingon sees himself as quite prepared to kill today, without remorse.

The threat of duels maintains a martial society officially at peace. The tradition insures that the quasi-religious warrior code of Kahless remains practical and doesn't degenerate into vague mysticism.

Most Klingons reject the notion of a Supreme Being. The duel circle is the closest thing to formal worship most Klingons get. Its highly ritualized combat adds rich layers of meaning. The formal duel is a "sacred" act.

The Klingon tea ceremony is another such ritual. A mildly toxic tea-analog symbolizes that death is best when shared.

Adult male Klingons can be challenged at any time. Weapons practice remains a necessity throughout the individual's life. An exception may be made for extremely elderly individuals as challenging one is hardly a courageous act. This also provides the Empire with a ready defense force since energy weapons are forbidden.

The dueling tradition also provides assurance that inferior males will not survive to breed children. Klingon women choose consorts who fight well or show promise of doing so. This "natural selection" is a secondary benefit of bat'telh tournaments.

Klingon psychology renders most conventional methods of maintaining civil order futile or costly. Klingons long ago confronted their violent natures and channel them rather than suppressing them. The dueling tradition offers effective social control without large numbers of police or troops.

Ritualized combat is preferable to random violence, impulse murder without proper challenge, or the destruction of non-involved parties to achieve personal vengeance. It is a highly practical means of enforcing behavioral norms.

Weapons

BAT'TELH The bat'telh is a large two-handed blade some Terrans irreverently liken to a set of steel moose antlers. It is the weapon of choice for most Klingon males outside active military service. This ancient weapon is practiced by almost every male youth. Its use in the duel is an extension of its use in tournaments. Mastery of this weapon requires a lifetime of practice.

Bat'telh drills are a Klingon analog of Tai Chi. Both practices feature slow, repetitive yet evolving movements demanding whole

FOCUS ON:

WHITEFANG STEAK The pungent, tender whitefang steak comes from a canine-like animal. Whitefang is served with the outside seared and a very rare center. It is served with various sauces. The dish is accompanied by traqs, small, sweet-tasting, slug-like creatures. Traqs are served live but can be killed for the squeamish. This highly recommended dish is only available in the winter.

body skill and concentration. Both derive from deeply traditional forms of martial defense, linking the practitioner more closely to this past with each practice session.

Bat'telh tournaments, military and civilian, are not an alternative to the duel. They give competitors a chance to evaluate potential opponents. Strong tournament showings lead to fewer duel challenges over an individual's lifetime.

LEV'EK The lev'ek, or three-lobed knife, is the standard dueling weapon aboard Klingon warships. Military personnel are trained in its use as a combat blade. Most carry one at all times. The weapon requires less space to use than the bat'telh, an advantage aboard smaller vessels.

The lev'ek is a primary weapon in informal duels, the Klingon version of a street fight, by enlisted personnel or Marines of any rank. Naval officers prefer a two-handed dueling form. They employ the lev'ek as a main gauche, or left-hand parrying blade, using a short sword with vestigial side blades as a primary weapon. Dueling swords are not worn as part of an officer's uniform.

There is art to skilled use of the lev'ek retractable side blades. It often spells victory in a duel. These blades are kept retracted until the last moment, when springs propel them deep into an opponent's joint. They may also be used as emergency sword-catchers or sword-breakers.

Some Klingons choose to duel with the Gin'tak ceremonial spear, a longer sword or a different bladed weapon. The only rule is that the weapons used by both parties must be roughly equivalent.

Powered weapons such as disruptors are strictly forbidden. The pistol duel of old Earth never became popular with Klingons. Klingon do not believe it allows a proper demonstration of skill and *klin,* roughly translated as courage. Poison is considered dishonorable. Either duelist may question his opponent's use of non-standard weapons, though this might be considered a failure of *klin.*

⟩ Duel Conventions

Reasons for a duel challenge vary widely. Tradition only requires that the cause be sufficient in the eyes of both parties. Most duels on Terra resulted from insult to a man's honor, lady, regiment/ship/commander, family, or dependents under one's protection. While this is the same in the Empire, they are changed by Klingon psychology.

Tokhe straay,' or "willing slave," is the most notorious insult challenge in Klingonaase. Questioning the legitimacy of birth or the species of a mother doesn't have much impact.

Inter-service rivalry—accusing a Naval officer of behaving like a Marine, or vice-versa—is a questionable but common provocation. Line-based challenges are the most esoteric, often involving ancient grievances. A family line member's failure to meet the behavioral standards of his line head, or *epetai,* may result in a challenge by kin seeking to advance themselves.

This last case illustrates an important point about challenges: a challenger's actual motive for calling out his opponent may have little to do with the reason cited. Political eliminations can take the guise of fabricated duels in the Empire.

Emotional entanglements can spur duel challenges, sometimes without the knowledge of at least one of the parties involved! In many cases the woman in question may be the covert instigator of a challenge, either to eliminate a consort she has grown tired of or to make her selection between two rivals.

⟩ Duel Preparations

Though several variants exist, the formal duel circle remains popular with military officers and higher-ranking civilians. The right to request such a circle is a fundamental, though unwritten, right of all adult Klingon males. Two days' preparations are traditionally allowed between the challenge and the duel itself: "One to remember, one to make ready."

A second, or cha'DIch, from one's own line is either selected or preferably volunteers. The cha'DIch is expected to check an opponent's weapons for venom or other irregularities, witness the combat as a line representative and arrange for removal of the body afterward if his combatant is unsuccessful. In rare cases, most notably Captain Jean-Luc Picard of the U.S.S. Enterprise, someone outside one's own line may be chosen for these duties.

The duel circle is inscribed on a gymnasium deck on most Navy ships. Combatants' attire resembles the Terran gi with loose trousers, sleeveless under tunic and wrapover padded tunic. The last is sleeveless but serves as a form of armor. The combatant also wears leather and metal gauntlets ending in fingerless gloves, used for blocking or parrying slashes. A line-sash or *kli'lakh* bearing family colors or devices is optional. Except for the sash, all dueling attire is traditionally black. No footgear is worn.

Duelists using the bat'telh rather than single or paired blades frequently choose sturdier gear or fight in uniform. Traditional dueling gear affords little protection against a bat'telh's heavier blade. Though gauntlets are often worn, they are obviously not used in parrying.

To The Death

After the weapons inspection, formal duel circles begin with a challenge embrace intended to demonstrate ferocity. Bared teeth, snarls and even rib-crushing are expected.

Participants then return to their own sides of the circle to begin fighting. Klingon dueling style shows aspects of both formal Terran European fencing and Oriental martial arts weapons forms. Heavy emphasis is placed on physical and psychological intimidation.

There are no strictures against "dirty tricks" or weapon-breaking. A broken weapon cannot be replaced once a duel has started. First blood is always cheered by spectators, though UFP citizens would be well advised not to follow suit.

Klingon duels always end in death. No quarter may be asked or given.

DUELING

The victor is expected to salute his commander, or the highest-ranking person present, by crossing both blades over his chest and standing at attention. Exact forms may vary. This salute is usually repeated for one's cha'DIch as line-witness. Only after the salute is acknowledged can the opponent's body be removed from the circle.

In rare cases, tradition permits a duel circle to be stopped before death occurs. This is only for reasons of extreme political importance. The ritual phrase to do so is *k'haaj!*, or "it ends!". In the past, only a seated Emperor or his highest ministers were permitted this privilege. Current use is limited to Klingon High Council Chancellors, certain Council members and line *epetais.*

The duel circle with paired blades is most common among Naval officers and higher-ranking noncoms. Most Marines, even those of command rank, scorn such formalities as effete. Their duels are fought with the lev'ek alone, with the two-day preparation period omitted. Marines, it is assumed, are always ready to fight. Those in a position to know have said that any distinctions between a Marine duel and a corridor brawl would be lost on most non-Klingons.

Shipboard duels occur as circles. Available space aboard most Klingon vessels permits nothing else. Planetside other forms may be used to allow combatants to demonstrate their mastery of the bat'telh or other larger weapons.

♪ Women and Tradition

Klingon women neither challenge nor accept challenge. This is not sexism but a holdover from the Empire's desperate past. Then a line's survival might depend upon the number and health of its childbearing female members. Expansionist cultures rarely risk their strongest breeding-age females to danger.

Men reject fighting a female as dishonorable due to a lack of female upper-body strength. Sexual dimorphism is not as strongly pronounced in the Imperial Race as it is in Homo Sapiens. Still few Klingon women stand as tall or mass as much as their brothers.

Refusing a challenge from a female would be seen as even more disgraceful.

Certain individual lines, particularly those maintaining a Marine tradition, permit their female members to duel. These circles are rarely witnessed by outsiders. Females from such lines are discouraged from challenging outsiders.

Some Klingon women resort to less overt methods of resolving personal differences. When formal challenge cannot be issued to a rival or enemy, women turn to assassination. Several of the Empire's most talented government assassins are products of this inequality.

The Kut'luch, a variant of the standard military lev'ek, is traditional for such purposes. Its use distinguishes the assassin from the mere murderer. The weapons are often left behind as a calling card. Fingerprints are carefully wiped away first.

A curious double standard exists concerning poison. Male Klingons shun it as cowardly. No such social stigma accompanies its use by women. Women are often valued for a knowledge of subtle and successful "applied toxicology." It is often regarded with pride by the assassin's line-kin, including potential consorts. This is how the Klingon axiom "drink not with thine enemy" arose. . . and why an invitation to a line banquet must be regarded with extreme caution by non-Klingons!

FOCUS ON:

KLINGON SALT WATER: Most races should drink a chaser with Klingon salt water. The drink is made of sea salt and tuber alcohol. The salty drink is very strong, approaching 200 proof. Without a sweet, syrupy chaser, most races will choke on this Klingon delicacy. It is highly recommended.

DUELING

⅃Cautions

Federation citizens are normally immune to duel challenges even on worlds of the Empire. This is less diplomacy than personal honor. Defeating an untrained and ill-prepared opponent shows little *klin*. Even in cases of considerable insult, the average Klingon would be more likely to simply pound offworld offenders to a bloody pulp. They reserve the privilege of the duel circle for their countrymen.

Captain Picard set a new precedent by acting as his Security officer's cha'DIch. This renders the UFP citizen's position more precarious. Tourists are strongly cautioned to avoid following Picard's example.

It is unlikely a Klingon acquaintance would even consider asking a human, or other member race of the UFP, to act in this capacity. It is not unheard-of for the respective seconds in one circle to become principals in another.

Along with observing extreme caution in matters of Klingon honor, travelers should keep their wits about them when visiting local drinking establishments. Klingon physiology differs from human in many respects, but not in its reaction to large amounts of ethyl alcohol.

Since synthahol is unpopular outside the Federation sphere of influence, unusual displays of weapons or "fighting words" should indicate an exit point. Not all duels are conducted formally. The line between spectator and participant often becomes extremely blurred.

Civil authorities often won't attempt to interfere with the ensuing melee. The mere explanation that a matter of honor is being settled is often enough to send them away. Most insurance policies available to Federation travelers do not include coverage for claims resulting from such an experience.

LEGENDS

by Lynda Phillips

LEGENDS AND TALES

It is the belief of the authors of this guide that visits to other parts of known space are enjoyed more by knowledgeable travelers. To that end we include the legends told on the worlds the traveler is likely to visit. NgoKnuur, and their home world of Nguu, as well as the individuals, species and worlds of these legends, never existed. However they do reveal much about the thoughts, beliefs and values of those who value the tales.

The legends tell a history of many clans. The history is one of struggle and conflict, treachery and triumph. Ultimately it is a revelation of the character of the peoples who tell the tales. This may be the only way in which a private people can reveal their most cherished beliefs.

This legend tells of powers and abilities that might be termed magical. It offers a glimpse at the mystical beliefs of the tellers.

CLAN AZHIN

The Q'Kadrak are a strange clan. Their origins are shrouded in the mists of Ancient NgoKnuur.

The clan is the last representative of a sub-race of Nguus called the "Halbskaal." They are characterized by an Imperial crest from the back of the neck to the summit of the skull, leaving the forehead smooth.

When a Halbskaal shaves their head, the ridges dominate. When they let their hair grow, they look like human fusions. They are often associated with fusions on missions against humans and came to trust human-fusions as allies and equals. Human fusions wishing to join the clan are admitted without prejudice.

Many hesitate to ask entrance into the clan because of dark stories linked to the name. The Q'Kadrak clan began centuries before the space age. The clan is so old it's difficult to separate fact from legend.

In those times, "Those who Destroy From the Darkness," the mysterious demons of NgoKnuur, reigned. The Q'Kadrak people were associated with them. The clan home in the marshlands of the small southern island was witness to many weird events.

The original name of the clan was "Q'Ka-Dakula." It contained a word used on many planets to suggest vampires. Q'Kadrak's founding fathers may have been vampires or sorcerers. They experimented with the darkest mysteries of the universe. Vibrations left by their incantations still give a special atmosphere to the grounds surrounding the ancestral home. Visitors are few.

Some used their powers against "demons" and "dragons." It was their contribution to the growth of modern Nguu civilization. Q'Kadrak people use their strange gifts on behalf of the Empire.

Kveld Q'Kadrak Azhin is the son of Kvass, a military instructor for the clan Q'Kadrak. He lives on the island "Q'Kadrak," on the home planet, NgoKnuur. Few visit this place of many tempests.

Kveld was adopted into clan Azhin shortly after his birth. Due to the similarity between the two clans, he was not required to sever his links with clan Q'Kadrak. This double heritage is allowed by the traditions of the Azhin clan. He is not entitled to talk of the mysteries of clan Azhin, being only a junior member at this time.

The legend of a clan told through the tale of its most important member. The story indicates which traits are prized in clan members.

CLAN BODDHI

My grandmother, also named Vixis, was born on the Northern Wastelands of NgoKnuur. This was not an auspicious start in life.

Once the wastelands were great—the Empire was ruled from here and the North was the powerhouse behind this rule. Over the last century things had changed. The center of government moved West.

The Northern Lands remained frozen in time, the populace surrounded by the decaying grandeur of Empire. Poverty hung so thickly in the air, one could almost reach out and touch it. Musty odors of damp and rot were always perceptible. There was little employment for our warrior people. They whiled away their lives drinking, brawling and gambling in they many clubs and bars.

Grandmother ran away when she was still a child. Lying about her age, she enlisted in the Imperial Navy. Over the years, she fought her way up through the ranks, ending up as Commander of the IKV Okrona.

The vessel was in the charge of the now famous Captain Klaa whom, at the time, Vixis greatly admired. Later, Klaa became an intergalactic hero for pursuing a Federation craft, the U.S.S. Constitution, across the Great Divide. He performed a previously unheard of act, and rescued its Captain from certain death. After this action, Klaa became a popular figure within the Federation.

Tentative moves had been made in some quarters towards a pact between the Empire and the Federation. It was decided it would suit Imperial purposes if the ruling family were to appear more Federation friendly. Towards this end, Klaa was accepted into the House of the Emperor as sole consort of the eldest daughter.

LEGENDS

All this was unfortunate for grandmother. During the voyage she had let her passion for Klaa get the better of her and she now carried his child beneath her belt. This was discovered as her girth increased. She demanded more than her normally paltry food ration.

Klaa denied paternity. Not wishing to push the case for fear of condemnation by the ruling family, grandmother fled to her homelands in the North.

Here she bore a son. She named this son Krian and provided for him by hunting for furs in the great wildwoods. Because he had no father, Krian and his immediate descendants were lineless. This went unnoticed in the wastelands as many others were in the same position.

When Krian grew to manhood, he inherited a farmstead when one of Vixis' uncles died. It was not good land, but bleak and situated on top of a windswept hill.

The house was old and rambling. It always felt cold, despite the fire burning in the great hall. Krian raised enough crops and livestock to just scrape out a living.

At the local year games he met his future consort, Annick. She was a hefty, redoubtable woman who had won the regional knife throwing contest. When she was not throwing knives, she worked as an attendant at the internment center for the criminally insane.

The bonding of Krian and Annick was fruitful. They produced seven sons and one daughter, myself. I was named Vixis, after grandmother.

It was not easy living with seven brothers. Day to day existence was a constant struggle against a rising tide of discarded socks, half drunk flagons of ale, gladiator matches on the holovision set and avoiding their interminable fights.

I would take refuge in grandmother's room, and listen spellbound to her tales of life amongst the stars. I vowed to follow in her footsteps one day.

Eventually, grandmother was killed in a hunting accident. I inherited her few belongings; her knives, Naval uniform and log books.

For some reason, unlike my brothers, whom all wanted to be Marines or gladiators, I showed a flair for academic work. I was admitted into the North Western Academy. There I embarked upon the study of the Sciences of Life.

The Academy was located in the Citadel on the Western most Shores. The citadel was a strange place, its wealth gleaned from the trade in Kuve. This practice had been outlawed long ago, so the citadel's fortunes had collapsed. Now the place looked as though it were in the aftermath of some nuclear holocaust.

Great tracts of once grand buildings were either reduced to rubble or burned out, boarded up hollow shells. Amongst the litter strewn bombsites rose great marble mausoleums, incongruously surrounded by neatly kept gardens.

Everywhere was damp and dripping. It either rained or smog obliterated the lurid red sky, so it always seemed to be dark. The inhabitants of the citadel had come from all regions of NgoKnuur and some other planets as well. Every conceivable color of skin, hair, and every possible type of head crest could be seen there.

Many revelers roamed the sodden streets at night, screaming and roaring. They were watched over by two monolithic temples on the black pavement, unheeding of the rain.

The citadel was a stopover point for many ships. It was here I met my first consort, Kron. He was an officer on board a battle cruiser. Like grandmother, he was full of fascinating stories of space.

I graduated with honors from the academy, and returned to the North. There I obtained a job as a scientist in a genetic engineering plant. We were working on fusion techniques, splicing DNA, inserting this into cells, culturing them and manipulating the creatures with radiation as they grew.

I stayed here for many years. Eventually I became bored by the routine and worried about the effects of the high doses of radiation on my body.

I obtained another job as an instructor at a local training institution. I soon picked up the skills necessary for a career in teaching, such as withering sarcasm and the ability to hurl chalk with unerring accuracy. I taught anatomy and became famous for my dissections that were always carried out live. The screams of the alien as I strapped it to the bench and wielded my scalpel never failed to wake up the acolytes in the morning.

I enjoyed my work. Often as the students labored over their anatomical drawings, my mind wandered to the stars and the excitement to be found there. Many of the students found careers there. I often heard stories of their deeds.

During his final leave, Kron brought me a present. On his last mission he was involved in some sort of altercation with a Federation ship. He was part of the group assigned to search the vessel for survivors. During this search they heard a keening noise coming from the hold. On investigation, it turned out to be a newborn baby. Kron claimed it as a spoil of war and brought it back to me as an amusing plaything.

Ordinarily I would have toyed with it, then tired of the sport and dispatched the child. Somehow, though, it wormed its way into my affections. Now I have an adopted Puun daughter named Jana.

This was the last I was to see of Kron. He was blasted out of time and space by the Gins, leaving me in the normal state for a Nguu woman. . . widowhood.

I decided my time had come and signed up to join the Navy. Much to my amazement, I was accepted on provision I completed "Top Up" training to make me eligible for Medical Services division. I packed my few belongings and caught the trans globe shuttle to a new life.

The Medical Top up course Officer Training School presented few problems. Mother's advice on knife throwing came in useful during combat skills. After a year I graduated, hardly a Thought-Master of medicine but more a mere bone setter, able to effect very basic repairs. Neither was I a great warrior, but well able to take care of myself.

My cadet cruise was not glamorous. I worked as a sick bay assistant on a freighter hulk, the IKV Chuvmey, shipping provisions to space stations and isolated colonies. This did not bother me though, for I was amongst the stars and already had witnessed many weird and wonderful sights.

It was on such a supply mission to station Gamma Six that I inadvertently acquired my Terran surname. Most of the crew had been granted an evening's leave, and on that particular night, representatives from many ships and planets were gathered on the base. Special entertainment all the way from Terra had been laid on; dancing and music from real musicians.

As I looked around the hall, I wondered why species from such far flung galaxies appeared so similar. Humans, Gins, Puuns and Laos all had the same basic look. These philosophical thoughts were soon banished as I drank heavily. I hurtled violently around the dance floor. The last I can remember is standing on a table and removing my uniform, watched by a cheering crowd.

The next morning, I awoke disorientated. I was shocked to find myself in a totally strange cabin. I stretched out along the heating device next to the berth and it moved and snored loudly. I gave it an exploratory prod with my dagger, and discovered a human male.

I hoped I had had a good time the night before, as I pushed him out of the bed. When he hit the floor, he woke up, and very kindly made me a cup of a drink called tea. We tried to piece together the events of the previous evening.

Apparently we had been married by the Captain of a passing Federation ship, his idea of a joke no doubt. This was legally binding, so I now bear the Terran surname of Boddhi. Luckily the human and I discovered we were compatible, on the rare occasions we saw one another. I did not get much leave and authorities on Terra wanted to impound him for crimes linked with smuggling and gun running. Any time we had together was spent evading the authorities. There was one memorable event when he stowed away on the freighter to which I was assigned.

My time in the Navy, so far, had been uneventful. I had seen no active service. I had always performed any task I had been given to the best of my ability and I had never been in trouble with my senior officer. So, after a few years, I was upgraded to Tai status and soon after, what I naively thought was the golden opportunity for further advancement, came my way.

I was offered sole command of Medical Division on board the scout cruiser IKV Maswov. We were to be the only ship on an expeditionary mission into Gin space. Our aim was to secretly glean information.

Events did not take a glorious turn. I was grievously wounded and spent a month near death, plus many more months hospitalized. Our mission became the focal point of a major political wrangle. The

Commanding Officer, Rebekkha, was accused of treachery. The trial still awaits resolution and I hear High Council is taking a vote upon the matter.

Now I am fully healed and have been assigned to the KSF on Terra. There I serve in the Medical Science Division. I presently live within the Kingdom of Northumbria with my daughter, Jana. It is a cold, gloomy place.

There is a Starfleet base in nearby Newcastle City that I am keeping under careful observation. I await further events with interest.

The clan symbol of Boddhi is a winged serpent. Clan Boddhi adopted this symbol, as it represents Vixis' Terran Consort's homelands and he is descended from the Lambton Line.

The legend of the rise and fall and rise again of a now powerful and respected clan. It indicates a belief in redemption.

CLAN D'MAU'TAH

Merak, the First of Clan D'Mau'Tah, left his home in the city of Aval, on the home world of NgoKnuur, during the wars of Axanor. Merak's mother and father asked him to stay, saying that the Space Fleet was corrupting their people. He joined the Imperial Marines Division of the Military Fleet.

The Clan of D'Mau'Tah has served the Empire loyally for countless ages. They work as Intelligence and Security Personnel.

After enlisting, Merak sent for a replica of the shield that had held his family's line symbol for almost 700 years. Kata, the third successor to Clan D'Mau'Tah, had inscribed two crossing battle blades, covering them with an Imperial Trefoil. He proclaimed that "From this day forth, forever shall this shield be the symbol of our Clan; letting us know that even as we are all individuals, yet are we a single unit, and as long as this shield shall stand, so shall we know that we are never truly alone."

The shield passed from one generation to the next. It remains virtually unchanged.

Merak fought bravely in the wars. He returned to Aval to honor his line by bonding with the one he had been promised to at birth. His heart beat with anticipation as he awaited his mate from Clan Dristal to arrive with her family. Traditional Clan introductions began upon the arrival of the clan from the planet D'Rokar.

When Merak was introduced to Kadrea, his mate, he could not believe his eyes. Before him stood the most beautiful Imperial female he had ever seen. The bonding ritual was performed that afternoon before Kask, the D'Mau'Tah Family Line bearer. It was conducted in the D'Mau'Tah Family Temple, a shrine to Kaiyaket the Ubiquitous.

LEGENDS

Two years after bonding, they again gathered the families of D'Mau'Tah and Dristal in Aval, the ancient Homeland of Merak's family. Much feasting and celebrating followed Kadras' announcement she was with child. During their stay in Aval, Kadrea gave birth to a son and heir to the Line.

Merak named his son Kurak, "The New Hope," for it was written in the chronicles of Kask that: "There shall be one among you born, that will be a great warrior, a new hope. He shall bring glory and victory to our people and line. He shall be called Kurak!"

Kurak followed his father's path to the Fleet Academy during his twelfth year. Thus began a new era of greatness for the Clan. Although Clan D'Mau'Tah still dedicated itself to the Security and Intelligence Divisions, it would now also face the challenge of space.

Kurak was assigned to the IKV Wicked Fortune for his one year cadet cruise. The ship was attacked by two Gin Scout Class vessels during his fifth month aboard. Kurak assumed command of his vessel when his Captain died during the first onslaught of disruptor fire.

Kurak rallied his crew to victory. The captured Gin Commander was subjected to hours of interrogation and the mind scanner. Then he was taken to the Homeworld for execution before the Council.

Kurak received the Award of Valor, the Sword of the Empire Medal and command of the Wicked Fortune. The posting is considered an unprecedented achievement by a first year officer.

Kuras began intimate relations with his navigation officer, Keras, during his first command of a training mission. The Imperial Nguu female had been born to Duran Berata and Vekar Trekan of Clan Berata. When Keras graduated from the academy, Kurak requested her assignment to his Wicked Fortune. Kurak loved her and could not bear to have her far from his side.

During their third year training mission together Keras recognized her love for Kurak. They returned to the Homeworld to be bonded after she told him. Through the influence of their fathers, Merak and Duran, they persuaded the High Council to allow them to be bonded in the Great Hall of the High Council of the Nguu Empire. Only the leader of the High Council, the Council Members, and the parents of Kurak and Keras were present for the ancient ceremony.

Keras gave birth to a son during the next season. Krell, the warrior child, would find a great destiny.

He entered the Military Fleet Academy one year after the age of Inclusion. Four years later he graduated in the top 1% of his class, earning an official commendation for outstanding efforts.

During his cadet cruise, on a mission to Karon II, he met an eloquent and astoundingly beautiful Nguu Female. He observed her bathing in a secluded lake. He discovered she was Kitrall of Clan Surwaq. Krell silently vowed he would make her his mate. Never before had a woman ignited such savage fires as burned in his deepest soul.

His high academic achievements and excellent cruise performance allowed him to secure an assignment to the defense outpost on Koran II. Kocha, a mutual friend, gave Krell an introduction to Kitrall.

Kitrall was instantly attracted to him. She was stirred almost to the point of arousal by his presence. He told her of his burning desire and they made love the entire night, held fast by ecstasy's grip. The next months were spent happily courting.

When Krell wanted to bond with her, he went to M'Dak'Taj, the father of Kitrall, to ask his permission. This was the traditional sign of respect.

LEGENDS

M'Dak'Taj gave his permission. One month later they were bonded. The bonding took place in the Suvwag family gardens, a place of beauty and mystery. The parents of Kitrall, M'Dak'Taj Surwaq and his mate, K'Shai Melkotz-Surwaq of Clan Surwaq, attended. Krell's commanding officer stood in for Krell's parents. They had both been killed in battle while attending a Cardassian peace initiative meeting.

The initiative was a cowardly attempt to break through the empire's defenses one ship at a time. Krell's father destroyed four Yipuun ships before greeting his death in the cold depths of space. He had lived his life among the stars and among the stars he died.

The D'Mau'Tah line became very powerful and mysterious through their victories. Ancient stories told to the children of the line stirred the soul to great victories. Kitrall's parents were pleased their daughter bonded to a fine warrior.

Krell was recalled to the Homeworld shortly after the bonding. He returned as a great warrior and a husband. Krell was approached by Koral, a prominent member of the High Council. He was authorized by the leader of the High Council to offer Krell a seat on the Council. Krell readily accepted.

He was the first in six generations to hold such a seat. His family had not pursued political power. Krell believed it was time for the D'Mau'Tah to regain the status lost long ago.

During his reign on the council Krell fathered three children, two boys and a girl. Kitak, the eldest of Krell and Kitrall, was the only one to enter the Fleet Academy. Kitak graduated with honors and served various defense outposts before transfer to the Global Security Divisions of the Nguu Strike Force.

Kitak hopes one day to be offered a seat on the council. For now he is content with his current assignment.

His sister Versai and his brother Kral are the owners of the posh night club, Suvwi'Tah, the Enduring Warrior. Only the rich and powerful frequent this club. Council members and even the Emperor enjoy its fine cuisine.

Thus ends the line history for Clan D'Mau'Tah.

A clan member tells how her clan expanded to the stars, and united with another clan.

CLAN DORIG-DOK'MAAR

I am not sure of the exact date, but it should have been about 2 1/4 centuries before my birth when my Great-Grandmother, Zul'ta Dorig, inherited the Family title, line, and holdings, due to the untimely deaths of both her parents. She was in DIS 15 at the time. The family ran smoothly for the first year. The mines, the main source of income for the line, prospered. They did not show full profit.

Zul'ta, an Imperial, knew she could not run the mines and manage the family alone. She would have to choose a mate. After many weeks of serious consideration, she chose a particularly dashing and daring Imperial male known throughout the area as K'rangleth Zandle.

If family lore is to be believed, he would have been a privateer. The leader of a band of four capable bandit ships raided throughout the galaxy. Zul'ta wasn't shy about her intentions. She proposed the consortship to him.

K'rangleth knew a profitable situation when presented with it. He wasted no time in accepting. An agreement was reached within minutes. He would accept the Dorig line name; partly because of his profession, and partly because Zul'ta refused to accept his. He would supply the necessary labor, and tools for the mining operation. The Dorig line would give financial backing to his ships.

Within four years of the consortship, the mines became extremely profitable, making the very small Dorig Line one of the richest on Kahz. The bonding also resulted in two children.

The first was a daughter. Vad'upla took to the field of science, becoming one of the Empire's top scientists in bacterial diseases. It eventually killed her at age 42.

The second offspring was a son, Kezhon. He entered the Academy, and graduated a year early, with honors. His cadet cruise was on board the IKV Doom. He then went onto command school. On his first day he met Kroxia Dok'Maar. He felt an instant attraction to the young female assisting the Commander of the class.

Kroxia was a Fusion by birth. By Nguu standards, she was absolutely stunning, and extremely intelligent. She made those around her feel at ease. Kroxia was pointed out to the High Council as a possibility for Imperial Intelligence.

Kezhon spent two years studying. He became a good officer and commander. He put equal effort into winning Kroxia. Competition for her was high, but he felt himself fit to the challenge, and believed the prize worth the effort.

Kroxia took a chance the day before graduation. He used the personal code of the class commander to peek at the final grades. She was stunned to find Kezhon first in the class. She had thought she would be #1, not #2.

She had never met anyone as determined or as handsome, as the young Imperial. He had presented himself to her constantly throughout the two years. She thought he would make a good addition to the Dok'Maar line. The morning of graduation she presented the idea of bonding. Kezhon accepted. They had not anticipated opposition from both lines.

The very rich Dorig's did not have the political clout the Dok'Maar Line wanted. They were considered beneath the Dok'Maar's. The leader thought Kroxia's looks and intelligence could do better. The Dorig's, on the other hand, were not thrilled with fusion joining the family, and ending a line of Imperial blood.

After many months of arguing, Kezhon and Kroxia took matters into their own hands. They informed the High Council of their decision. The Council was not thrilled with the possibility of losing two of the Empire's star pupils. Kezhon was offered a new ship, and the chance to choose his own crew.

A meeting was then requested of the two lines, bringing them together one last time. Kroxia and Kezhon, by mutual agreement, gave both sides an ultimatum. Either they could accept the consortship, or work out a fair agreement, or the two would forsake both lines and begin one of their own, with the council's blessings.

An arrangement was worked out within three hours. Neither family wished to be on the losing end of this relationship. Kezhon would accept the Dok'Maar name and take half of the Dorig family holdings. Upon the death of his parents, he would inherit the other half. In return, the Dok'Maar Line would ensure the protection of the Dorig Line, and upon the death of Zul'ta and Krangleth, adopt the rest of the clan.

Commander Kezhon and first officer Kroxia ran many very successful missions for the Empire. The crew of the IKV Duy'A'Bortas worked well together, quickly becoming known in the fleet for their daring and cunning, as well as their ruthlessness. The first four years resulted in many commendations, 'The Star of the Empire' medal for bravery, 'The Open Daggar' for personal valor, and one son, Krigarro.

Kroxia gave up her post alongside Kezhon and returned to Kahz. She remained there until Krigarro entered the Academy.

His studies put him in the field of intelligence. He applied himself for first six years, not allowing anyone to get in his way as he climbed the ladder of rank, taking his key personnel with him. When he made Colonel, he was assigned a new assistant, Lt. Key-Tira Kerleth, from Internal Intelligence. At first sight, Key-Tira knew she wanted Krigarro as her own, not only as a consort, but also to help her up through the ranks.

Krigarro resisted at first. He did not want a weak female clinging to him. After three years of faithful service, he realized she was anything but weak. He finally gave in, and the consortship took place.

They lived a long and happy life together, having one son, K'Erst. He was born on H'Rez while Grandma was there on assignment. The assignment took two years to complete. At the end of the assignment he was sent to Khaz to be raised by the line, as grandmama refused to leave grandpapa's side.

Within two years, she presented Krigarro with another child. They named their daughter, K'Landa.

K'Erst disappeared one year after graduating command school. To this date, his fate is unknown.

K'Landa attended the Academy and went into the field of medicine. At one point, the inhabitants of Mera-Zine were dying from a strange bacterial disease. The area was under quarantine. After many hours of simulated programs, and computer analysis, she thought she had found the cure. She informed the High Council, and requested clearance to transfer to Mera-Zine, to test her treatment. She arrived and immediately began to treat those around her.

Within two days, an Imperial scientist arrived and began to treat those around him with an unproved cure. This created many arguments between the two. She was sure he had no idea what he was doing. He was, after all, a scientist, not a physician.

Several 'patients' began to get better. When questioned as to which treatment they had received, both were shocked to find that they had treated the same patients.

Within a few days, using both treatments, the situation was under control. Further investigations revealed the bacterium was accidentally set free by a cadet on a training mission.

The Emperor was so impressed with their work, he had them both transferred to Delta Khinah II to work on other projects for the Empire. A consortship began shortly thereafter. The result was one daughter, Kimpla. She recently transferred to the Nguu Strike Force, where she is serving in the capacity of Ambassador.

NOTE: While serving in this position, Kimpla uses the last name of Dorig. This prevents any problems with the Federation and their allies, as they may be aware of the Dok'Marr's opposition to the Federation.

CLAN DRACLON

Draclon is one of the oldest blood lines. It is the most murderous and evil of all clans. Dar Draclon's ancestors practiced the black arts. There is even talk of Lakshman worship.

Trouble started many hundreds of years ago, when the eldest brother, Zarton Draclon, left to fight in a great war. He left behind his younger brother, Darrag Draclon, and his wife, La'Tor.

Darrag Draclon lacked honor. He entered a pact with Feclar during Zarton's absence. He also seduced his brother's wife and made her a willing partner in sadistic murder. They unleashed dark, uncontrollable powers within the walls of the Castle Draclon. Soon no night passed without screams of torture echoing through the castle walls.

Years passed. Finally a victorious Zarton returned home. He was not prepared for the terror that awaited him at his castle. When his wife kissed him, he beheld a cold dead look in her eyes, but chose not to mention it.

As they entered the great hall, La'Tor left Zarton's side to embrace Darrag. He stood waiting for them, along with their eight year old son, Felar.

Zarton saw admiration for Darrag in his wife's eyes. This enraged him. He drew his sword to slay them all, but the fatal blow never came. Instead Zarton sank to his knees in pain, a victim of his wife's poisoned kiss.

They laughed at his final moments. The dying Zarton slew his brother, plunging his sword deep into Darrag's chest.

Standing beside the dead brothers, the young boy Felar, inheritor of Darrag's powers and evil ways, smiled at his mother. From that day on, the line of Draclon was cursed.

LEGENDS

Felar eventually took a Gin female as his wife. The balance of power within the Nguu Empire swayed slightly towards the Draclon's until Felar's death.

Unknown to Felar, Tor'rad Draclon was with child. She vowed to regain the Draclon name. She gave birth to a son and a daughter. She named the son Zahn Draclon and the daughter Sthenno Draclon.

Zahn became a great military leader. He died in a mining incident on Praxis. Sthenno learned the Draclon's way of darkness. She never took a mate, but she gave birth to a son she named Karius.

Karius's features were more Gin than Nguu. His dark eyes showed no emotion. Karius enrolled into the Imperial Star Academy. He turned to espionage after graduating. As had his forebears, he took a Gin as wife. They had twin sons, Tor and Dar.

Tor Draclon wanted to serve the Empire. He enrolled in the Imperial Star Academy at the age of 12. His brother, Dar, knew his destiny waited elsewhere. With his grandmother's assistance, he became the fourth Draclon to hold the title of "Mortum Hesta."

He enrolled in the I.S.A. He joined the C.O.C. after graduating. There he discovered plans for an assassination attempt by renegade Nguus against the High Command. He was given the rank of Lt., and the Honorific of Sutai, for saving a member of the High Command.

Few knew the assassination attempt was Dar Draclon's idea. At the last moment he thought it best to foil it, and did. Dar Draclon remains in the C.O.C. with the rank of lieutenant. He often returns to Draclon Castle to be instructed in the dark powers by Great Grandmother Sthenno.

Tor Draclon recently took a Nguu bride. They have had five children. The line of Draclon is strong but lacks influence. Dar knows he shall one day sit upon the High Council. Then the name of Draclon will be felt in every corner of the Nguu Empire.

This legend was purportedly written by an Admiral Kian Zantai Jiraal, a member of the clan. Perhaps it is newer than other legends.

CLAN JIRAAL

The clan Jiraal claims the planet K'arith Prime, in the K'arith system near K'lai NgoKnuur, as their property. They have been in service to the Emperor for one hundred years.

Membership in the Jiraal Line is limited to the fusion races. Our tradition is service to Security and Intelligence branches, Naval and Marine. Some line members serve in the KDC. A small number in each generation are educated as personal Thought Masters of Genetic Medicine.

We believe the true glory of fusion races within the Komerex is doing what our races were first created for: interpreting, infiltrating and subverting the UFP and the Gin Star Empire. These skills have been supported by the Emperor and the Imperial Council or Senate over the decades. Competent information gatherers are valued by all political leaders. Not all glory is gained in overt combat.

The Clan has no official line symbol or markings. Some members use the DNA halifax with broken ladders to signify the clan. Those who use this symbol for their own purposes disappear under mysterious circumstances.

There is a line-maxim for clan members: Strike From Shadow. Clan Jiraal numbers between 10,000 and 12,000, with slightly more human than Gin fusions. Information regarding the exact size of the clan is classified.

The current epetai is a human fusion, Governor-General Kiarnn of K'arith system. Gin and human fusions have served as clan epetais. Cooperation between the fusion races is a tradition. The Clan does not believe in Nguu racial superiority, though it currently holds political power within the Imperium.

The most noted clan member in recent history is Rian Jiraal. She was born on K'arith Prime, the only child of human fusions. Her parents died gloriously for the Komerex during her early childhood. Their names and the circumstances surrounding their deaths cannot be revealed due to the sensitivity of the mission. This is common when clan members die in the line of duty.

Rian was raised by her uncle, Kithras Sutai Jiraal, because both her parents were frequently on assignment. He is a veteran covert Specialist whose glorious record ended when he was exposed to an experimental nerve gas. Although his lungs were ruined, his knowledge was highly valued by the clan.

She was educated in the Linehold with her line-brothers and sisters (cousins). Following her uncle's advice, she studied Galacta as a child. She was highly skilled in Psychology, the social sciences and Armed Personal Combat.

Her studies in the social sciences inspired her to write in her free time. Her Uncle disapproved, but this skill later proved useful.

She entered the Star Academy after completing basic studies. Her line warned her of prejudice against fusions. She overcame this by showing great skill in Languages, Interrogation Technics and Theory and Cultural Studies.

She completing her studies. The Academy Evaluators selected her for the Security branch of the Navy. They changed her name to Kian.

Her early training and line tradition prepared her for the work. She excelled in Psychology, Negotiations-Diplomacy and Surveillance.

At the age of 17 she brought glory to her line. She graduated in the top 5% of her class, and in the top 1% of Security branch candidates.

She was assigned to an Imperial Navy patrol of the Federation border during her first tour of duty. She served as Security Chief-Coordinator for Kaath's squadron. After discovering Sompop falsifying records, she set up a surveillance system to prove her suspicions. Sompop's subordinate Captains were made aware of this information. The commander of the Starboard Wing became Squadron Leader following Sompop's summary execution.

She was then assigned to infiltrate a UFP outpost on Starbase 10. She sent useful information to the Empire through a contact on the outpost's supply ship. She learned that a fully equipped Starfleet medical team was due to conduct routine physicals. She carefully removed her surveillance equipment, notified her contact and got off the base just in time. She secreted two explosive devices that destroyed the primary life support system of the post a week after she left.

She was given her first command as Intelligence Specialist-Commander when she was 27. She was assigned to a "merchant ship" operating in the Triangle near Federation influence. She was to collect intelligence regarding buildups of Federation Troops, material and research installations on UFP controlled worlds. Her ship, coded Shadow Dancer, turned in productive reports.

During patrols she contacted a ship, coded Dark Horse, Commanded by Captain Koryo. She met a human-fusion, Security Chief Katalyia K'Tore, aboard the Dark Horse. K'Tore impressed her with her attention to Security Details. She kept an eye on K'Tore, noting that line Jiraal could use someone with her abilities.

She contacted Katalyia K'Tore after she returned to her homeworld and inquired if she would like to join the line Jiraal. After considering the offer, Katalyia accepted the adoption, changing her name to Katalyia K'Tore-Jiraal.

Both Kian and her adopted line sister, Katalyia, continue to bring honor to their respective clans.

Further information regarding the history and activities of the Line Jiraal is unavailable.

This legend tells of a clan born off the home world, on a colony world. This must be a very new legend indeed.

CLAN K'JUDANJA

Born on Kannaga, my family line was awarded the control of the planet, after years of battling the Kinshaya, along the Coreward frontier. A family line, once a million strong, now only numbers a few thousand. Emperor Karan, may he always be glorious, awarded our epetai, Korman, the command of the Kannaga outpost, and the Seven Battle groups posted there. The line symbol of the Clan is Worlds in a Palm of a Hand.

Korman's four sons and three daughters survived Karan's drive for the throne. Each commanded one Battle Group. My mother was one of the commanders. My father has long since "retired," fighting a delaying tactic with a Kinshaya Foraging Fleet.

Life on Kannaga was a challenge. The world lacks minerals, much like NgoKnuur. It made the very young mindful of waste and misuse of resources. The world is strategically located near the Federation Boarder, within striking distance of the Orion Colonies and the Triangle.

Each young K'Judaja child is instructed in the Martial Arts. Military Tactical Theory was taught as a core curriculum during the teen years. Those who could not pass the Academy Entrance Exams were conditioned into the NCO ranks. They were given proper assignments to insure they would not pass on their defective genes, but instead retire in battle.

Koryo graduated in the top 20% of the classafter studying Computer Systems Technology, Computer Operation, Electronics Technology, Interrogation, Galacta Language, Orion Language, Marksmanship (awarded the Silver Hand of Kah), Unarmed Combat(reigning Overall Champion at the Academy), Small Unit Tactics(awarded Emperor's Cup at the Annual War Game Tournament), Starship Strategy/Tactics and Federation Law (Thesis—How to make the Federation Violate its Own Prime Directive.)

CLAN KMERVA

The Kmerva line is new. The line achieved high status within only three generations. As a child, the founder, Kel, was left in a House for Lineless Youth. He was a ward of the Empire.

He did not excel in his studies. Instead he played on his House's Klin Zha Kinta team as blockader. He brought much glory to his House.

Kel was surprised to be accepted for the Imperial Star Academy when he was twelve. It is not unusual for Lineless Youth to be accepted. It was rare for an individual to enter with no known assistant.

Kel did not care for the mystery. He wanted to know if someone would later demand repayment.

Kel began a cautious investigation. It later proved valuable. The assistance came from General M'Tal Indiz.

Kel learned M'Tal may have been his grandfather. M'Tal's son fathered a child before his death. The female, Katha, was the daughter of M'Tal's greatest rival, Katec. An agreement was reached that if Katec permitted the child to live, the child would be placed in a House for Lineless Youth. M'Tal would never have contact or assist his grandchild.

Kel wisely didn't approach his grandfather. Instead he worked hard to obtain better grades than his classmates.

Kel was rewarded with a cadet cruise. He was assigned to the *Blood Burn*. Kel brought many battles. His ship patrolled the Gin boarder.

Unfortunately, he did not have the opportunity to distinguish himself in battle. Kel completed his training and graduated first in his class. He took the line name Kmerva.

Kel's was assigned to Ambassador Korpe S'Tra as Security Attaché. He soon decided the Ambassador's only daughter, T'Al, a Naval Attache and Chief of Staff, would make a suitable mate

He began a campaign to win her. Six months later T'Al became his mate. This formally joined the S'Tra and Kmerva lines. Kel became Chief of Korpe's Staff.

Ambassador Korpe was killed a year later, after the birth of Kel and T'Al's only child, Keas. His diplomatic shuttle exploded without cause. Through the Right of Inheritance, Kel gained Korpe's position as Ambassador. Kel had no patience for diplomacy and turned the Ambassadorship into a seat on the High Council.

It was falsely rumored Kel had plans to displace the Head of the High Council. Kel knew his survival chances were better as a member, instead of its head.

Kel carefully planted incriminating information against the Line of Katec. When Katha faced the Council, Kel met privately with her and offered a way out in exchange for his rightful inheritance.

Katec and M'Tal were long dead. Katha's mate and sons had also perished. Kel reminded her that she had two choices, dishonor or honor. Either way he would receive his due.

Katha agreed. Kel promised she could live out her years in comfort.

Kel was now a powerful individual. He insured that his influence and wealth remained intact. While Kel stayed on the Homeworld at

Council and later as a Senator, he insured that his son was properly trained for entrance into the Imperial Star Academy.

After graduating from the Imperial Star Academy with the rank of Ensign, Keas took assignment to the Expeditionary Forces. The Imperial Navy had begun construction on the planet Mastocal. They planned a large Naval Base. Ensign Keas became instrumental in the base's design. He was also promoted to Lieutenant.

Kel paid his son a visit, informing him of an arranged mating to J'nfir, daughter of Thought-Admiral K'rul M'aee. The father was then one of the most influential individuals in the Imperial Navy, and had jurisdiction over Mastocal.

Keas was not happy with the order from his father to mate this an unknown female. He obeyed Kel's wishes under duress. After the bonding and formal joining of the lines, Keas was promoted to Captain. He was named Base Commander.

Under Keas, the building of Mastocal stayed on schedule. He imported kuve labor. When the Puuyings halted work in the installation, Keas was not baffled.

He began construction again a year later. This time he said Mastocal would be used as a medical base for the Quadrant. The planet lies close to the Gin border. The Puuyings failed to stop that conflict so the Nguu Navy desperately needed the hospital.

At this time the Empire learned the Puuyings were not infallible and could be fooled. Keas was promoted to Admiral, named governor and given Mastocal as his own. Keas had two sons and two daughters, Krmax, Indiz, Keath and J'nif. Krmax, the eldest, was sent to the Academy. Keath followed.

Keath quickly rose through the ranks. He gained the rank of Captain within six years. He was given his own command, the Bird of Prey, *Imperial Glory*.

Keath used his Homeworld of Mastocal as a base. After his father died, Keath inherited the loyalty of six squadrons, his brother Krmax, the Governorship of Mastocal, and six squadrons controlled by Keas.

Keath gained fame for his battle skill, cunning, honor and patience. He patrolled the border with the Federation. Early in his career, Keath used cunning to trap a Gin spy. The spy was sent to a newly colonized world to poison its water supply.

A second born son, Keath was fortunate that his father did not feel the need to arrange a proper mate. He became interested in T'era Batlh. After her mate was killed for the glory of the Empire, Keath made his interests known. T'era became his only mate within a month.

Keath grew to love T'era's daughter, Y'Kirah. Keath offered her the Rite of Adoption, which Y'Kirah accepted, feeling that Keath was her only father. Keath had one other child, the daughter Tevram.

Keath's patrolling ship picked up a distress signal from a Federation shuttle. Keath led the landing party that found Ambassador John Paul Jones and his son, Matthew Jones.

During preliminary interrogation of John, one of the shuttle nacelles exploded. Keath would have been killed, if John had not pushed him out of the way. Keath was amazed. It took time for him to understand why someone would save the life of an enemy, and lose their own in the process.

Keath transported both humans to his ship, ordering the surgeon to save John. Before John died, he asked Keath to protect his son, Mat. He wanted Keath to see that his son returned to his family on Earth.

Keath felt a debt and granted this request.

An urgent message was received from Mastocal at this time. The Gins were attacking. Keath raced home to defend his world. By the time the Imperial Glory arrived, the Gins had been defeated.

Keath found the Governor's Complex destroyed. He learned that his brother had been killed when the planet's shields had buckled and the Complex took a direct hit. Keath was now Governor through Rite of Inheritance.

Keath's mate and children survived the attack. He gave T'era charge of the human child, Mat.

Mastocal was put in order and the necessary reports made to the Council. Keath settled into the Governorship and Senate seat, formerly held by his brother. He named Kari, his brother's mate, as his assistant.

Then Keath offered the Rustai to Mat. He explained that John's act of honor had prompted this offer. The Rustai was performed and Mat Craig became his brother, due the honor and respect of everyone on Mastocal. Keath began to work with the Puun Ambassador on the Home World to return Mat to his family on Earth.

It took three years to accomplish due to bad relations with the Federation. During the time, Y'Kirah and Tevram grew attached to Mat, as he did to them. Although younger and smaller, Mat took the honor of protecting his line sisters very seriously.

When Keath announced the Puun Envoy would soon arrive to return Mat to his human family, all wished it did not have to be. Mat refused to leave. Keath who reminded him of his promise to John. He was honor bound to fulfill it. Only then did Mat agree to leave his Nguu home.

LEGENDS

A year later, Y'Kirah came to Keath, asking his aid entering the Imperial Star Academy. Keath advised his daughter and assisted her in the Academy.

Keath retired from the Imperial Navy as an Epetai. His time is now spent between the Imperial Senate and Mastocal.

Y'Kirah took the name Kirah on graduating from the Academy. She quickly became indispensable to her ship, Bird of Destruction, and Captain Kenzi Zantai Q'Tar. Her cunning forced a Starfleet Captain to make a formal apology to the Empire. Later she developed a strategy that saved not only her ship, but the colony on K'Karr. She was accepted into the Nguu Strike Force where she now serves.

LEGENDS

This legend of a warrior clan is obviously told by a martial people. The story, supposedly recounted by a lieutenant, may indicate how the tellers saw their enemies.

CLAN KORESH

The line of Koresh began with my great-grandfather, K'Bure. He was raised in the city of Aval on NgoKnour by a lineless, but loyal, family.

Life on NgoKnour was good to K'Bure. He wanted to serve the Empire. Proximity to the Northguard Naval Base prompted him to serve his people by joining the Imperial Navy.

K'Bure submitted his application to the Imperial Academy upon reaching the age of ascension. He was accepted into service. His wanted to become an officer. None of his forebears ever achieved this. He trained with great enthusiasm.

K'Bure's ambition drove him through the incredibly harsh physical and mental training. He was drafted into the Imperial Marines after graduating. This broke tradition. His forebears had served in the Imperial Navy.

His cadet cruise was a routine patrol along the Nguu-Chin border. The mission wasn't what K'Bure had hoped for, but he performed well. Upon his return, he joined a Marine Detachment based at the Darbva Defense Complex.

Years passed but K'Bure's dream burned as strong as ever. He waited for an opportunity to prove his worth and become an officer.

Rumors spread that a large exploratory force had disappeared without a trace along the Empire's border. The ships were exploring a rift area of space where few stars existed when communications were lost.

A new exploratory force was sent. This force also vanished. Other expedition disappeared in the same area of the rift.

K'Bure learned of a fourth exploratory expedition. He immediately requested transfer to the force. His transfer was approved. He was assigned as Sergeant to a detachment of Marines under the command of Captain Maraz. He was assigned to a support vessel, the I.K.V. Tolak.

No sign of the previous expeditions could be found for several days after they reached the rift. Only an extensive, long range scan picked up a faint sub-space signal originating from deep within the rift. They set course to intercept the signal.

The expedition soon found itself surrounded by hundreds of black globular vessels. The onslaught proved devastating. The exploratory force fought valiantly but couldn't match the superior capabilities of the alien vessels.

The Tolak remained behind the main force. It made a wide sweep to the flank to pick up wreckage from a destroyed alien vessel. They discovered what appeared to be the body of an alien crewman. The alien awoke aboard The Tolak. The alien immediately attacked the crew. The creatures could even withstand the vacuum of space.

The resulting battle killed most of the Tolak's crew, including all but one officer. Captain Maraz was ripped apart by the enemy's powerful claws.

Only Lt. jg. Konj Vestai K'Til, the communications officer, remained alive. As the most senior marine, K'Bure formed the remaining marines into a firing line. They joined Konj and his remaining staff and killed the alien with massed disruptor fire.

The Tolek returned to NgoKnour. It delivered the body of the alien. Its race was named Hiran by the expedition commander.

K'Bure was promoted to Lieutenant jg and given the honorific of Tai. After his promotion, K'Bure took the line name "Koresh." Koresh was the name of an ancestor.

The Hiran war died down to a few skirmishes along the border. K'Bure's regiment was transferred to the I.K.V. Bereya, a patrol ship along the UFP border. There he met his first wife, Mira, a first generation Nguu-human fusion. She served as Science Officer.

K'Bure's family was displeased with the bonding. They believed hybrids inferior to the true Imperial Race. To them, mating a half-breed was sacrilege. Despite their protests, the bonding proved fruitful. They had a son called Kislath, and a daughter, Kori.

Their consortship was ill-fated. Mira died in action in the Battle of Thranstor. Kislath and Kori were sent to live with Mira's parents on D'Rakar.

K'Bure returned to NgoKnour to await his new assignment. His Clan pressured him to take a second wife, K'lyr. K'lyr, a full Imperial Nguu, was much younger than K'Bure. She worked in the civilian diplomatic service.

Shortly after their joining, K'Bure left for the I.K.V. Kaiyaket, an L13 Battleship, operating near the Triangle. Not wishing his new consort to suffer the same fate as Mira, he left K'lyr on NgoKnour.

The ship detected an enemy vessel crossing the Neutral Zone. It moved to attack only to find several Warbirds decloaking around them. The Kaiyaket fought well but was out-matched. K'Bure died unaware K'lyr was carrying his child.

Distraught at the loss of her consort, K'lyr left her homelands on NgoKnour. Heavy with child, she settled on Kannaga as part of the civilian Colonization Project. She pleaded with the Gods to give her a son. Shortly after her arrival on Kannaga, her prayers were answered. She called the boy Tarag.

Kannaga yielded few minerals or ores. The atmosphere was too thin for agriculture. The planet still held a unique position of immense value to the Empire. Kannaga was very close to Federation space

Many Naval Bases were established on this world. Cities serviced the military. The only way to survive was to enter military service or to serve the officials at the bases.

K'lyr entered into service to an Admiral Kudek. Kudek had served in the war with the UFP, gaining many victories. The Nguu-human Fusion was well respected in the Empire.

Tarag was lucky. Kudek had no children. He treated Tarag like a son, giving Tarag insight into military life and service to the Empire. Kudek sponsored Tarag into the Naval Academy. Tarag specialized in Navigation and Helmsmanship.

After graduation, Tarag was assigned to the I.K.V. Okrona as Helmsman. He became friends with Commander Vixis, the Okrona's First Officer. Vixis taught him tricks with the Levek. Most of the crew, including Tarag, became enamored with Vixis. Tarag knew Klaa, the Okrona's Captain, had first claim on her. Loyalty to his Captain was more important than personal desires.

Routine patrol missions along the Neutral Zone were not what Tarag had hoped for. Still, life aboard the Okrona was rarely dull. The new Captain, Klaa, regularly ventured into Federation space to seize prizes.

The ambitious Klaa had two desires. He wanted to engage a Federation Starship in battle, and he desired his First Officer, Vixis. Rumors about their relationship ran rampant among the crew. None dared speak of it openly.

Klaa was the youngest Captain in the Empire. He had received the Okrona as reward for his actions along the Chin border where he proved himself the best gunner in the fleet. Captain Klaa still operated the weapon systems himself, something the Okrona's gunner, Morek, despised.

Morek came from a powerful family. He opposed Klaa in all things. He also desired Vixis. This proved to be his downfall.

Vixis was aware of Morek's ambitions. She didn't know how far he would go to fulfill them. She also didn't know the power of Morek's clan. His son, Mortag, was offered a seat on the High Council. Despite her suspicions, she remained silent.

A situation arose on Numbus III, the planet of Galactic Peace. Terrorists took control of the only settlement and seized hostages. One hostage was the Nguu representative, General Koord. The Okrona was dispatched to Nimbus III to rescue Koord.

Tarag's heart pounded at the chance for action. A Federation Starship, the U.S.S. Constitution, was also dispatched to retrieve their representative. Klaa had always wanted to engage a Federation Starship. Here was a chance to fight the best they had.

When they reached Nimbus III, they learned that the Constitution had just left with the hostages. Tarag set course to pursue. He discovered that the Constitution was on a direct course for the Great Barrier. They would surely be destroyed. Tarag reported this to Klaa, who insisted the pursuit continue.

The Great Barrier loomed ever closer. Tarag's suspicions grew. He suspected the Federation had developed a new shielding system. He scanned the Constitution's shields, discovering that they had undergone a dramatic alteration. Tarag brought this discovery to Klaa's attention. Tarag restructured the Okrona's shields to match those of the Constitution.

Morek thought the ship would be destroyed trying to cross the Great Barrier. He decided that his time had come, but he needed help. He wanted the Captain distracted while he made his move.

Vixis was the only one capable of this. Surely, she would choose the safety of the Okrona over loyalty to Klaa. He told Vixis his plan. He would kill Klaa while he slept. She pretended to go along with the plan.

When Morek left, she went to Klaa's cabin and informed him of the treachery. Klaa could easily kill Morek, but it was dangerous to kill the father of a Council Member. A Council Member with an influential Clan could put Klaa in a dangerous position.

Somebody else would have to kill Morek. The only person Klaa could trust was Lt. Tarag Vestai Koresh, the Helmsman. Klaa remembered Vixis saying that he could handle a disruptor. This would be his chance to prove it.

Tarag reported to Klaa's cabin at 0200 hours. He was not surprised to find Vixis sleeping in Klaa's bunk. Klaa told Tarag of Morek's plan that he must kill Morek on sight.

Klaa slipped back into his bunk. Tarag, uncomfortable yet slightly amused watching his commanding officer slide into bed with Vixis, drew his disruptor pistol and stepped back into the shadows.

Much later the door of Klaa's cabin opened. Vixis stirred at the sound, but Tarag trained his weapon on the figure standing in the doorway. It was Morek. Morek leveled his pistol at Klaa and Vixis. Tarag killed Morek. Klaa congratulated Tarag on a fine kill. Their mission could continue.

After following the Constitution across the Barrier, General Koord declared a truce and ordered the Okrona not to fire. They were to rescue the Constitution's captain from the clutches of a malevolent entity on the planet below. This action disgusted Klaa, but made him very popular with the Federation hierarchy.

An alliance with the Federation loomed just over the horizon. Klaa entered the House of the Emperor as consort of the eldest daughter. This was a veiled attempt to make the Emperor look more friendly to the Federation.

Tarag became Captain of the Okrona when Vixis mysteriously fled to her homelands on NgoKnour. Many believed she carried Klaa's child and feared condemnation by the ruling family. She removed herself from possible danger. Tarag believed the rumor to be true.

A young female, Me'Vel, became the Okrona's new weapons officer. Tarag fell for her. He took her as his consort. The bonding produced three children. The firstborn was my father, Krag, followed by another son, Tolag, and a daughter, Ga'Ros. They were sent, shortly after their birth, to be raised by their grandmother, K'lyr, on Kannaga. Tarag and Me'Vel continued to serve aboard the Okrona.

Ga'Ros was tragically killed by a wild Targ while hunting as a child. A very young Tolag was forced to bond to Azet'Ril, the daughter of a merchant. The couple had been caught in the throngs of passion by her father. He demanded their immediate betrothal.

A daughter, Koraz, was born. They soon left Kannaga with Azet'Ril's family and settled on Rigel III. Business was more profitable than on a military planet.

At the age of ascension, Krag, like his father before him, entered the Naval Academy. He excelled in most things, particularly security and interrogation techniques. Upon graduation, he was made a security officer on the I.K.V. Deathwing, a front line battle cruiser.

Krag developed a fine reputation. He excelled in his duties and was named in several reports to the High Command. Krag was promoted to Lieutenant, and then Security Chief aboard the Deathwing. It appeared Krag had a promising future. He might even one day receive his own command.

Then fateful news came. Mortag, the son of Tarag's enemy, had ascended to the Ruling Council. Days later, Krag received a report that Tarag, his father, and his mother, Me'Vel, had been found dead in their quarters. Their murderer was never identified. Krag knew Mortag was behind their deaths.

Things would grow worse for Krag. Against the protests of his commanding officer, he was mysteriously assigned as Security Chief to the notorious penal asteroid, Rura Penthe. It was a very serious demotion for Krag. He knew the order came from the High Council, from Mortag. Krag's only consolation was that his brother Tolag and his family would be safe on Rigel III, far from Mortag's influence.

The temperature on Rura Penthe took Krag by surprise. He expected cold, but this was worse than he could imagine. He couldn't believe any creature could withstand such cold. Overhead Rura Penthe's three suns glowed like pale eyes. No heat came from them. Warmth was only a dream in this merciless environment.

The prisoner complex stood below the surface. Krag found a variety of species. Chin, humans, Puuns; many he had never seen before. The scum of the galaxy were now in his care. The prisoners were sentenced to mine dilithium for the rest of their lives. Krag believed he had gone to Gre'Thor, the hereafter, where dishonored Nguu go after death. Mortag was determined to destroy the line of Koresh.

Krag made the best of his bad deal. He used his antiquated office as his quarters. He worked hard, serving the Empire, and building a good reputation.

Eventually he met my mother, Ki'Rel. She served as a medic on a visiting supply vessel. Their relationship developed during the vessel's visits to Rura Penthe. Eventually they bonded.

Ki'Rel remained aboard her vessel. The two met when they could. Shortly they produced two daughters, A'Gez and J'Tal, and a son, me, K'Mar.

My two sisters went to live with Ki'Rel. I remained with my father on Rura Penthe. I was raised on the asteroid. During my childhood I learned about the Empire. I also learned security procedures and armed combat from my father and the other guards. I even defeated my father once at bat'telh. As a reward, he gave me a duranium brooch, fashioned into our clan crest, a levek formed into the Nguu Trifoil. It once belonged to my Grandfather Tarag. Now it is mine.

As I grew older, I began to sneak out of my quarters and mix with the prisoners. I learned many combat styles. The most useful things I learned were criminal techniques and alien languages. I could pick pockets and make incendiary devices from easily available ingredients. I was able to get into or out of anywhere I chose. In short, I had a formidable knowledge of underground crimes across all known space.

I practiced the broadsword, levek and bat'telh with the guards. I wrestled with Ghuun prisoners, practiced ancient Terran Martial Arts with the human prisoners and often practiced with a disruptor pistol on escaping Chin prisoners. I became deadly.

Despite all this, I soon tired of existence in this bleak place. After reaching the age of ascension, I began to plot my escape. A transport vessel was due in a couple of days. The electronic shielding around the prison mine prevents the use of transporters, so a shuttle would be sent to deliver new prisoners. I formed a plan to disguise myself as a guard and stow away aboard the shuttle.

LEGENDS

During the two days, I stole pieces of uniform from various guards, and a levek and a disruptor pistol from the armory. When the shuttle arrived, I was ready.

The new prisoners were accompanied by six guards. Hiding in the rocks above one of the passages, I waited for my chance. The shuttle guards, after depositing the prisoners, made their way back up the passage towards my hiding place. As they passed me, I reached for my pistol. The rearward guard was a short way behind the others. When he reached my position, I launched myself over the rocks.

I landed behind him. As he turned, I brought the butt of my pistol down on his head. He slumped to the floor. A trickle of blood ran from a crack in his skull. I checked to see if he was still alive.

I took his cloak and mask and hurried to the shuttle. As we boarded, the pilot greeted us with some unpleasant remark about the stench of our clothes. I grunted in agreement and made my way to the prisoner hold. There I concealed myself for the journey back to the transport ship. I was not discovered.

After waiting a few hours, I checked the landing bay. Since arriving on the transport, I had heard nothing. There was only one inattentive guard. I made my way across the bay, towards a large maintenance hatch.

After opening the hatch, I discovered it led to a cramped crawlway. I slowly made my way into what looked like a cargo hold. It seemed an ideal place to hide. I climbed through and replaced the hatch cover, then hid behind unmarked cases. Feeling safe, I fell asleep.

I awoke to the sound of shuffling near where I was lying. It was dark. I drew my pistol and waited. It seemed to be searching for something.

I crept towards the sound. Something kicked the pistol from my hand. Shocked, I instinctively turned, only to receive a vicious punch from my unknown assailant. As I hit the floor, I rolled and quickly climbed back to my feet. I was now prepared.

I faced a large Nguu. He was not one of the crew. His next attack was a right cross. I blocked easily. In the same action, I gripped his arm and twisted. I now had him in an arm lock. I drew my levek and swiftly brought it to his throat. I was about to cut it, when a smaller Nguu appeared. He shouted not to kill him.

He explained that their names were T'Kar and Yeto. They were bored with their lot and deserted in search of fortune. They stowed away on the transport hoping for adventure. They had been drinking Saurian Brandy, finished what they had, and were searching for more when I disturbed them. I released my inebriated prisoner. We settled down with a bottle of Warnog and talked.

I discovered that they had settled on becoming mercenaries. After learning of my talents, they asked me to join them. The thought of adventure amongst the stars appealed to me, so I agreed to go with them.

We spent the next few days gathering weapons and provisions. One fateful day, the transport entered orbit around a small world. This provided a perfect opportunity to escape. Later that night we made a break for it. After dispatching some of the crew in amusing ways we stole a shuttle craft and launched a new career in space piracy.

We needed a ship. While on Rura Penthe I had heard that the best person to see was a Hunan dealer named Omag. He frequented Amarie's Bar on Qualor II. We set course for the Qualor system.

Omag was the most repulsive little creature I had ever seen. This was quite some feat. I told him we needed a small, maneuverable ship. He invited us aboard his ship.

He took us to his supply yard orbiting Qualor IV. The only ship he had fitting our requirements was a K-4 Gunboat. He had just taken possession of it from the ship yards at H'Rez. He asked us to make an offer. Drawing my disruptor, I offered him his life. I gave him no time to protest, but drove my clenched fist into his hideous face. He fell and knew no more.

The next few years brought a fortune in stolen booty. We looted derelict starships, taking their anti-matter for explosive devices. We supplied Ultritium to Antidean terrorists. Once we attacked an Angosium freighter and took their supply of Cryptobiolin.

I took a dose of the drug, hoping to benefit from its effects. Unfortunately the drug appears to be ineffective on Nguus. We used our talents to perform contract assassinations, espionage and sabotage.

One fateful day we were contacted by an agent from the traitorous Imperial NgoKnour States, located in the Triangle. They wanted us to break into the High Command's security system to retrieve information.

We went to NgoKnour disguised as Naval Officers and beamed down to Command Headquarters. Our forged security papers were very convincing. They got us past the guards at the entrance to the security complex.

Yeto was an expert at breaking into computer systems. He learned his skill during his assignment in Imperial Intelligence. He soon made copies of the complete network.

After returning to our ship, we decided to make our own use of the stolen information. After taking his money and flushing our former employer through an airlock, we examined our prize.

There was a particularly interesting file on my clan. I discovered all about the incident involving Captain Klaa, Morek and my grandfather, Tarag. I also learned about Mortag's son, Morek, and the vendetta against my clan. I learned that most of my clan had escaped Mortag's revenge.

My two sisters, J'Tal and A'Gez, were still alive. A'Gez had become consort to a marine officer, while J'Tal had turned from military life, became a disciple and settled on Boreth.

The human Fusion side of my clan was also flourishing. Kori had bonded and had a son, Kra'El. Although Kislath had become First Officer aboard the I.K.V. Terror, he had attempted to mutiny and was now languishing in a penal colony.

My heart was set on revenge.

I beamed back to the surface of NgoKnour. I used my talents to enter Mortag's household. I found the old man asleep. Although there was no honor in killing an old man, he would pay for what he had done to my clan. He would pay with his life.

His eyes flicked open as I neared him. My hands found his throat before a sound passed his lips. Lifting him from his bunk, I pinned him against the wall, and regarded the pahtk with the contempt he deserved.

He was old and weak. I easily held him with one hand. I drew my levek with the other. My cloak fell open to display my grandfather's brooch. Mortag recognized it immediately. He began to claw and kick.

LEGENDS

The blades of my levek snapped open. I thrust the blade deep into his chest. Mortag's body went limp as he slumped to the floor, uttering my line name with his last gasp. Vengeance was mine. I left as silently as I had arrived. My family honor had been appeased, but not restored.

After returning to my ship, I headed for my cabin and a bottle of Chech'Tluth. My mind raced even as I lie in a drunken stupor. I wanted to restore the honor of my line.

I decided to join the Imperial Navy. T'Kar and Yeto took the news well, especially when I gave them most of my share of the booty. They told me that they had been contacted by a Truul, named Verad. He wanted to hire them for a mission. Then they planned to head for the Gamma Quadrant.

Taking some of my ill gotten gains, I departed for the capital city. Once there I bribed an official and entered the Imperial Navy.

I excelled in Alien Languages and Culture and in Security and Interrogation techniques at the Academy. All that I learned on Rura Penthe proved most useful. I was best in my year group at unarmed combat, and the use of archaic weaponry, specializing in the levek and the broadsword. The hardship I endured on the penal asteroid prepared me physically and mentally. I was large and powerful, terrifying other cadets and some instructors. Few challenged my title. Fewer survived to tell the tale.

During my cadet cruise I was assigned as a security guard to the I.K.V. K'T'Mara, an upgraded D7-S cruiser commanded by Captain K'Tan, a human Fusion. I proved to be of great use to the Captain because I mixed easily with the crew. I listened and learned from them, and reported everything directly back to the Captain.

I helped foil an attempt to mutiny. I had heard several of the Imperial Nguus talk about how insulting it was for Imperials to be commanded by a human Fusion. They planned to kill him and seize the ship that very night. I informed Captain K'Tan of the plot. The perpetrators were slowly and painfully put to death in the Agonizer Booth. None of my crewmates knew I had betrayed them. I recalled that my father had told me how my grandfather had once saved the life of his Captain during a similar attempt at mutiny. Reports of my very useful skills soon reached the ears of those who mattered.

I was assigned to the Nguu Strike Force, an elite unit operating on Terra. Although information on my mission is highly classified, all should know I work for the Empire. All those who plot in secret, beware, for the ears of K'Mar Koresh are everywhere.

This legend also comes from a time before peace came to its tellers. It tells of a clan of fishermen who became intelligence operatives. It clearly offers an insight into its tellers.

CLAN K'TA'RI

The Keel K'Ta'Ri is of recent acclaim. The house of K'Ta'Ri is less than five generations old. The clan began in the city of Distanda, on the planet NgoKnuur, on the island of 'New Continent.' My forebears controlled a fishing fleet of moderate size. It numbered ten to twenty vessels at a time. They sailed the oceans for months at a stretch, catching great schools of Funaukua. Fishing was an honorable trade for a Nguu not serving in the Military. It was similar to battle. Each day brought new challenges.

Clan records lack detail about this generation. They only record ownership of the fleet, giving no names, lines or properties. Perhaps my line had been imprisoned at the Silvi Penal Colony for political crimes. When freed, they may have fled to Distanda.

Before the time of my great-great Grandfather, political unrest shook the Empire. Officers and Senators rose and fell, lived and died. I do know the family fleet made good money. The line established great wealth, bought estates from dislodged Senators and secured lands from officers and lines sent into exile.

After the death at sea of my great grandfather, S'Kor K'Ta'Ri rose to prominence. He sold the fishing fleet and used the wealth to buy lands on an island, the future home of the Darbva Defense Complex. S'Kor made numerous trips to nearby island to develop his lands. He sent managers to his other lands to check on his caretakers.

As the K'Ta'Ri Clan prospered, they came to the attention of the Senate. A powerful land owner can control many issues in the Senate. S'Kor was voted in as a new member against his wishes. He willed his properties to his son, Jols K'Ta'Ri. His son continued the family tradition of buying new land.

Jols bought properties on the Southern Islands, near the fledgling Deathstrike Base, along with a few small properties on other islands. He also bought land on the major continent. S'Kor K'Ta'Ri handled the paperwork for Jols.

S'Kor bought the favors of other Senators. He used their political clout to get his son, Jols, into the Military as an advisor on Cultural and Economic Affairs.

Jols loved the Military life. He was sent to help the farmers of Lantos. Jols established himself as the foremost authority on economic affairs within the Navy.

After S'Kor K'Ta'Ri died of natural causes, Jols returned to NgoKnuur to bury his father. Jols prepared Mardor K'Ta'Ri for life in the Navy. Mardor learned quickly. He enjoyed training, and was quickly accepted into the Academy at the age of twelve.

Jols left immediately for K'Tazza VII. Mardor could now control his own life. It was the last time Mardor would see his father. Jols disappeared under mysterious conditions while serving the Empire on K'Tazza VII.

Mardor graduated the Academy and went directly to Command School. Then he used the wealth of the K'Ta'Ri Clan to buy captaincy of a light cruiser. He sought fame, taking his ship and crew into the Triangle. Mardor had successfully by-passed the chain-of-command and made off with an Empire ship. This posed a problem to the Empire. He was now a wanted Nguu.

Mardor engaged the services of many independents. He used the authority of several planetary governments to obtain sensors needed for prospecting in the outback of the Triangle.

During seven years of prospecting, Mardor evaded many Empire squads. His quest finally ended when he discovered Dilithium

Crystals on Paxton III. He dispatched a message to Fleet Command through an intermediary.

Mardor returned to NgoKnuur. He was verbally rebuked. They reclaimed his ship and fined him several hundred thousand credits for his callous use of Empire materials and men.

Then Mardor met a civilian female named Keethra KiNui. They produced a son, Keel K'Ta'Ri. The family moved to the new capitol, New Khal City. The family now enjoyed established wealth, status and station.

Keel gained a cosmopolitan view of NgoKnuur as Mardor took the family on regular visits to their many homes around the globe. Mardor introduced Keel to high-ranking Senators and Officers of the Fleet. Keel formed friendships with many of the most important people.

Keel was easily accepted into the Academy. His command studies proved him to be of excellent caliber. Keel went directly into Command School after graduating. His Cadet Cruise earned him an excellent record.

Keel was selected for intelligence work. He served under Admiral Kmar and Admiral Kurkura in one of the many Strike Forces on Federation and Chin central planets.

Keel's wealth and background proved beneficial to the Empire. Nothing should hold him back from success. Keel now commands the Strike Force on Terra. It is of paramount importance to the eventual downfall of the UFP. Many Senators feel that diverting funds to this Strike Force will aid the Empire and advance their careers. Keel K'Ta'Ri has proven capable of solving seemingly insurmountable problems. The KSF will be the harbinger of death for the UFP.

 This is the tale of a clan that fought peace when it came. It may reveal the feelings of a minority opposed to a peace brought about by others.

CLAN K'TORE

The K'Tore Clan has been in existence longer than any member can remember. It began as individuals gathered for protection.

The Clan began on NgoKnuur, in an area just outside the major mountain range. It was chosen for its distance from a hostile civilization. As the band grew, it decided to choose a leader. After violent disagreements, Koran K'Tore was chosen to lead the band. They adopted his name as their common designation.

The K'Tore's prospered for several years. After a severe drought, they moved closer to the mountain range. Mountain streams would provide water for the clan. They chose a site at the bottom of a pass between two mountains. Koran noticed that the two mountains formed a point when the sun rose in the morning. A sword held in line with the mountains cast a shadow toward an easy route through the range.

The clan continued prospered under Koran's rule. Upon his death, his son, Kero, was chosen to take his place. The clan barely survived an attack from the rival Contani. Kero was one of the few survivors. He pulled his remaining people together, preserving the band.

One surviving Contani was taken prisoner. Kero interrogated the prisoner. He learned from his experience, and assigned his son, Keton, to be 'The Watcher of the Point.' Keton also designed a symbol for the clan to be used as identification. Others attempting to use the pass would be executed unless they had been granted safe passage by a member of clan K'Tore.

The clan again grew. With a guarding at the point, no surprise attacks could succeed against the clan. Kero's son Keton assumed command after his death. He assigned Kestra to be 'The Watcher of the Point.'

LEGENDS

Time passed. The honor of the clan was placed above all other concerns. Anyone dishonoring the clan name was disciplined. The discipline sometimes resulted in death. Like many other clans, they adopted the saying, 'Death Before Dishonor.' They taught this to their children.

When the Empire expanded to include the stars, the clan sent representatives. They attained high positions and brought great honor to clan K'Tore. When the Empire allied with the Federation, the K'Tore clan was outraged. The Epetai, Katal, encouraged them to accept the great honor of alliance.

Honor was put to the test when the decision to support the alliance was challenged by the new Epetai, Korla. He entered into a pact with Clan Kotrei without telling his own clan. They undermined attempts to strengthen the alliance.

The next in line for the position of 'The Watcher of the Point,' Kotra, learned of the dishonorable actions of Korla and challenged him. Kotra won, attaining the title 'Epetai.' She executed those involved in the dishonorable acts and struck all names from the records. The Kotrei Clan was also summarily executed.

When a position opened on the outpost of Khest, the K'Tore clan sent its best working team, Korson and Kareli K'Tore. Although Kareli was with child, they did not hesitate to report for duty. Korson and Kareli served with honor. Kareli gave birth to a daughter she named Katalyia in honor of the Epetai Katal. Fortune did not smile on them. The post fell to a Chin attack. Korson, Chief of Communications, issued a distress call to the Empire.

The Federation ship, the USS Huron, found one survivor. They identified the survivor as Katalyia by the medallion the child wore. The Federation crew searched for other survivors. They took every document, along with the child, in hopes someone at Starfleet Command could decipher the child's identity and locate her family.

The child was placed in the care of Bobby and Julia O'Brien. They had three children of their own, Johnny, Trisha and Robbie. Katalyia remained in their care for 15 years. Then the Federation finally located her family name, K'Tore. Admiral Robert Jennings, through Ambassador Kev'n Couins, contacted Epetai Kotra K'Tore. He informed her of the Nguu orphan, Katalyia O'Brien, found on the planet Khest.

Epetai Kotra reviewed the information and documentation. She decided to reclaim the child and change her last name to K'Tore. Kotra provided the Federation with transportation for the child's safe return.

Further investigation into the child's medallion revealed it was a modified version of the clan symbol. What the crew of the Huron mistook for a name was in actuality an identity mark. Epetai Kotra, aware the parents intended to name their child after the Epetai 'Katal,' ruled that the child's official name would be Katalyia K'Tore.

Further information on the Officer Katalyia K'Tore can be obtained through military channels. All other information is classified and available only to authorized personnel.

It appears that twins were a rarity for the people who originated this legend. This unusual clan was blessed with twins. This legend offers an insight into family.

CLAN K'TREN

The beginnings of the clan are shrouded in mystery. The first known member of the line was Wo'Qor. There was nothing to distinguish him as a child, except that he was the son of the second officer in charge of the mining operation on Praxis.

His parents were on duty at the duranium mines when the moon was destroyed. As one of the command personnel, Wo'Qor's father was blamed for the disaster. That he could not have prevented it did not matter. Wo'Qor grew up without family or honor.

He was known as the "Son of the Destroyer" in the orphan colony where he spent his youth. It was called only 'Lanbir,' or 'cold place.' It was located on the polar continent of Bezhag. Food was scarce. Relief supplies went first to the homeworld, then to citizens with honor.

Life was difficult throughout the Empire at this time. Natural disasters were only part of the problem. Peace with the Federation was not popular with most citizens. It was regarded as a necessary evil.

Survival was the pressing problem. An entire planet had to be relocated. Attention must be paid to each citizen's status and property. Thousands of Nguus killed each other over small pieces of land.

Life at Lanbir was worse than in most places. Wo'Qor grew strong. He learned to survive. The youngest died from starvation and exposure. Their bodies were left as bait to catch meat. Hunters lived while others became tools of the hunters. The brutal life taught skills needed to survive in the Empire.

Wo'Qor escaped from the colony at the age of fourteen. He killed the soldiers guarding the transport. He was accompanied by two older inmates. They commandeered the ship and forced the pilot to take them off world. Wo'Qor would spend the rest of his life as a pirate, an outlaw raiding many star systems. He stayed away from population centers of the Nguu Empire. His name was lost among thousands of other records in the tempestuous times.

Wo'Qor had twelve consorts during a period of twenty years. His planetfalls were many, although of short duration. He left many children behind.

Piracy was good to him. Before his death in battle at Bethia Prime, he sent messages to gather his kin. None of his consorts had been aware of the others. It was a fruitful meeting. There were nineteen sons and fourteen daughters. He bequeathed them a legacy of stories and wealth. He told them of his plan to win favor with the Empire. None ever recounted what was said at the meeting. It is known only that the siblings divided into groups and grew in numbers and wealth.

Qor'Ip was the third son of Wo'Qor, by an Imperial Nguu named SiStuj. He captured much wealth over the years. His business was outside the Nguu home system, his name unknown to the High Council. He bought enough land on NgoKnuur to become a major political force.

Many Council members tried to learn who he was. Once he moved to his lands, he kept his heritage secret. He seemed to be a member of the ruling class. He trained his children to take their place in society. He built a fine home and educated his children in the best schools. He loved intrigue. He developed a network of spies to rival that of the Emperor.

Qor'Ip was called 'The Quiet Lord' by the Council. They ridiculed his business ventures, but envied his success. Since he showed no interest in politics, others grew careless. They accepted his help in small things. He built a reserve of favors, and held them, quietly, for years.

Unlike his father, Qor'Ip had only one consort. He married late in life. The young woman bore him four sons, two sets of twins. This was very rare. Some took it as a sign of potency. While ridiculing his lack of martial skills, they gave him grudging respect. His consort, Mapegh, was the youngest daughter of a provincial governor. The marriage increased the family status a little. It mattered little to Qor'Ip. His plan for his sons was secure.

Kajrek, the oldest of the four brothers, was the strongest. He proved himself a worthy recipient of his father's lavish attention. He grew skilled at all he was taught. At age nine he killed a kuve on his father's estate that he caught stealing from his brother. He dragged the body to his father, and told him what he had discovered.

His strength and attention to honor determined his fate. Qor'Ip called in favors to have his son accepted into the Star Academy. It was the last time his father had to intercede. Kajrek distinguished himself at the academy. He was sent immediately to Command School.

Junior officer Kajrek proved himself a brilliant tactician with a cool head. His first posting was aboard the IKV Kor'yoh. They were sent to quell an uprising on Bezhag, the place his grandfather had begun. It had been turned into a penal colony. A transport crew occasionally grew lazy and underestimated the inhabitants.

Kajrek watched his commander rage at the uselessness of the mission. The command crew followed his example. When the attack came, they were unprepared. Pirates blindsided them. The commander and tactical officer died leaving the Kor'yoh helpless save for auxiliary power.

Kajrek had read about a trick in a stolen Federation text. He gave the order to cut all power and drift, feigning helplessness. When the pirates came in for the kill, Kajrek waited until the last moment, then blew them into the Black Fleet. As the crew made repairs, he gave the penal colony their last choice: surrender their weapons or die. They did not respond. He launched a barrage of torpedoes ending forever all resistance from the colony. The continent is still uninhabitable.

Kajrek received many honors, and a reputation for being in more than one place at a time. This was not true. The rumor was created by him and his twin brother, Qo'ris. They worked as a team in many ventures. Qo'ris protected the lands and property on the homeworld while Kajrek brought honor to the line, earning the status of Epetai.

Kajrek commanded five vessels in eighteen years. The last is the flagship IKV Predator. It serves the Empire on the Chin frontier. He had seven sons by his consort Velas. After her death, he adopted a child, a human girl.

The wealth of Clan K'Tren is overseen by the oldest brothers. They have made alliances with other descendants of Wo'Qor and enjoy connections to several High Council members. They keep power by adherence to the standards of the Empire, and a shrewd sense of business and politics. Their enemies know them as a reposing dragon, and do not take them lightly. The time of Clan K'Tren is coming, soon.

This legend tells of an important clan. The clanis one of inventors, not only warriors. The tale shows the value the tellers place on inventive genius.

CLAN K'WITH

Clan K'With is based in the Imperial Capital on the Nguu Homeworld, NgoKnuur. The clan advances technology on the planet. They formed the Guild of Mechanics and inducted every one in the clan who knew family secrets. Each person was given a choice: take the name of K'With or die.

Induction included adherence to strict rules about sharing this information with outsiders. Anyone breaking this rule was summarily executed.

The first head of Clan K'With invented machines similar to those of Earth including a steam engine, a system of aqueducts, flow controls, a parachute, a hand glider, a bicycle and an armored chariot pulled by animals encased in armor.

A later clan head was noted for inventing labor-saving devices, including the automatic loom, the threshing machine and the equivalent of the cotton gin of ancient Earth. The devices he invented freed warriors from toil. He later became known as M'ren.

K'Sin K'With pioneered the use of electricity. This led to early forms of communication devices and lighting. K'Sin was adopted into the line to prevent encroachment on family territory.

K'Than K'With achieved fame by inventing the Warp Drive. The Nguu Empire began exploring space. They eventually collided with the Chin Empire and the much despised Federation. Shortly before his death, he revised his theory, greatly improving the warp drive. It is still in use in all Nguu vessels.

Khen K'With witnessed the deaths of his parents, D'Hen and M'Rah, in a transporter accident. He was determined to keep it from happening to any-

LEGENDS

one else. He studied science at the Academy, paying strict attention to transporter technology.

He mastered Transportation Technology and Warp Physics. He also mastered the skills for communications and computers. He then created safer transporters.

Clan K'With specializes in Physical Science. If the founder of the clan was also an artist and biologist, these interests were abandoned in later generations.

CLAN RESHTARC

One hundred fifty years ago, Mandu Kor, epetai of the House of Kor, was a ruthless and iron-handed Merchant Prince. He bought and sold everything from computers to drell, an illegal substance then. He ruled his vast domain from a lavish Keep just north of the city of Khal. He stayed one step ahead of the Imperial authorities. The House of Kor built and supplied illegal parts for the newly founded Star Command of the Imperial Navy. The family made a handsome profit from corrupt senior officers filling their own pockets.

Mandu had many mistresses, but only one consort. Her name was Tel. She bore Kor one son, Morogoth. When Morogoth was a year old, Tel fled with him from Mandu's abode. She took refuge in small towns, remaining on the run, hiding from Kor, fearing retribution for bringing disgrace to his house. Kor was a rogue Nguu. Tel had higher hopes for her son.

Knowing Kor would eventually find her, she hid her son with the clergy of the Temple of Kaiyaket. She was discovered and murdered while working in a small village tavern. She would not reveal the location of her son even under torture. Knowledge of his whereabouts died with her.

Kor never found young Morogoth. He pursued Tel for revenge, not to find his son. Morogoth was four years old when his Mother died. He never learned of his parentage or the House he belonged until he reached the age of Ascension. Then the Clergy told him his identity. The Clergy urged Morogoth to disassociate himself from the dishonorable House of Kor. He wisely took their advice.

Morogoth chose the name of Reshtarc, taken from the mountain on which Kaiyaket delivered his speech of 'Honor Through Strength.' It is so written in the sacred text. Reshtarc dedicated his life to learning and teaching the words of Kaiyaket.

At 25 Reshtarc tried to discover his Mother's origins. The Northern Empire and the Komerex Dexi were engaged in the final war that would create the Nguu Empire. His Mother's house was located in Kaiy City, which had been the victim of nuclear bombing.

During this final conflict, Reshtarc went to a small fishing village of Koreim, now known as Southwatch. Koreim is located on the southern end of the main continent.

At 27 Reshtarc took a mate, Az'Mar Ja'Rook, the daughter of the village leader, Bider Ja'Rook. The Ja'Rook house held no importance. For the next 23 years, Reshtarc brought education and commerce to the small village. It grew and merged with two other villages, eventually becoming the City of Southwatch.

Az'Mar bore Reshtarc three sons, Torn, Barg and Khambata. The three boys continued their father's work. Torn and Khambata joined the Imperial Academy. Barg followed in his father's footsteps to become part of the Clergy of the Temple of Kaiyaket.

The House of Reshtarc became very powerful, along with two other houses, the House of Va'When and the House of Kruch'a. Reshtarc died at the age of 61 of a bone disorder. Khambata, the youngest and most politically powerful, became Epetai. He was a local hero, with victories over the new enemy, the Chins.

He would eventually rise to Admiral, commanding all naval forces along the Nguu-Chin border. He had friends who owed him favors in the Great Hall in New Kaiy City.

Torn obtained the rank of Lt.-Commander. He died in an incident while serving on a ship in orbit around Kobek. Kobek exploded during a power struggle between the Nguu Empire and the leaders of the Kobek outpost. The outpost stored an arsenal of old nuclear warheads.

Barg became the High Clergy of the Temple of Kaiy. His mate, Green Pa'Kue, bore him one daughter, Lurak.

Their mother, Az'Mar, died of natural causes at the age of 68. First, though, she would see the House of Reshtarc grow into a local political power.

By the time Admiral Khambata Epetai Reshtarc took control of the house, it had grown to over ten thousand strong. It absorbed the old village.

Admiral Khambata took a mate at the age of 39. La Sutai Va'When was an accomplished council member for the city of Southwatch. She did a great deal for the city, and supported major industries. She also sat on the Board of Masters at Southern Imperial College. At 35 she bore Khambata his first son, Koll. Two years later, the second son was born. They named him Kuller.

Both boys joined the military. They attended the Imperial Academy. Kuller graduated at the top of his class, the younger bother of an "All Academy Klin'Zai" champion, Koll.

Both served in the Imperial Fleet as officers. Koll achieved the rank of Captain, commanding the D18 Destroyer, the Black Knife. He grew to the status of Zantai. During the Four Year War, he served with his younger brother, Kuller, the commander of a vessel with no name. The vessel would become known as Blood of the People. Each ship chalked up over 29 kills before the war ended.

During the Four Year War, the House of Reshtarc supplied the IKN with over 3,000 warriors. Over 70% were commissioned officers. Reshtarc Industries supplied most of the sensor and targeting systems to the navy.

LEGENDS

Southwatch University was founded during this time. It was the last act of La Zantai Reshtarc. She died of a massive heart attack while giving a speech to the University Board and Faculty. A bust of her image was placed in the Hall of Masters. It is still on display.

Kuller took a mate during the war. Lt.-Commander Drall Sutai Dok'Marr-Reshtarc was an Imperial from the House of Dok'Marr. She was killed in the battle of Axainar while serving on Kuller's ship as his Security Officer. Kuller never took another mate.

Captain Koll stayed in the IKN. After the war, Koll commanded a Zee Four Defense Outpost along the newly formed Nguu/Federation Neutral Zone. He served Outpost Maska for fifteen years. Koll met his consort, Parania Tai Axaenti, at the outpost. The nineteen year old was working as a civilian bio-engineer assistant. Koll and Parania kept their relationship secret for a long time. They had a girl child, T'Veg.

The House of Reshtarc knew about Koll and his young consort. The reason for their silence is not clear. The Epetai and the Council of Elders didn't to 42 year old Koll bonding to a much younger female. They approved of his bringing new blood into the house. The current Epetai, a cleric of Kaiyaket, did make it known that although the bonding was good, the secrecy was not. It implied distrust of the House of Reshtarc to accept "outsiders" into its fold.

Koll was barred from contacting his family for one year as punishment. Parania and T'Veg were summoned to NgoKnuur to live and work in the community and the House of Reshtarc into which she had been bonded. Parania was then pregnant with a boy, later named Drell. A year later, Parania and the children moved to Memphis Gamma Two, where Captain Koll was stationed as Planetary Governor. They stayed for seven years.

During this time, a plaque of Admiral Khambata Epetai Reshtarc was placed in the Great Halls of the Empire for his devotion to the Nguu people. The Admiral died in an attack on Khaz, while commanding the Fifth Fleet against the evil Federation. Admiral Kuller was given the honor of unveiling the plaque. He remembered that day as the proudest day of his life.

The House of Reshtarc continued to grow, not only in its Reshtarc Industries, but also Southern Imperial College and Southwatch University. The Imperial High Council considers the school to be one of the top ten Universities in the Empire.

The Temple of Kaiyaket grew as a direct result of the House of Reshtarc. Believing a true Nguu can not prosper without honor, the House of Reshtarc donates 30% of its profits to the Temple of Kaiyaket. Seven new Temples were opened throughout the southern region of the main continent.

The city of Southwatch grew to three million people while the House of Reshtarc grew to over 23 thousand. Kuller, a respected member of the High Council and Epetai of the House of Reshtarc, closed the House to non-Imperials. He believed it important to keep the House pure. There was much debate. Finally non-Imperials could join the House only by bonding with a family member. They could never hold a zantai or epetai status. This kept the House hierarchy pure-blooded Nguu.

Captain Koll became Admiral Koll and transferred back to NgoKnuur as Base Commander of Dabvara Defense Complex. Much had changed. Haud Epetai of the House had died making Kuller the new Epetai. This caused unspoken friction between the brothers. Koll felt shamed that his younger brother was a powerful High Council member promoted to Admiral before he was. Now his younger brother had risen to the status of Epetai. Koll was also very proud of his younger brother.

LEGENDS

Admiral Koll insisted that his son Drell, now twelve, enter the Imperial Star Academy, the premier institution in training military officers for the Empire. His daughter, T'Veg, was already enrolled at Southwatch University. She studied bio-engineering.

T'Veg died in a tragic accident in a lab experiment. Her class was pioneering inter-structural transporting, so common now. T'Veg and her classmates were honored for making the theory into a reality.

At eighteen, young Drell, now known as Krell, was commissioned an Ensign in the IKN. He was assigned to a D-9 Light Cruiser, Ka'Broug, as the Assistant Chief Engineering Officer. He also received the status of Tai. Two years later, Ensign Krell fought the battle of Comar Six. He received a promotion to Lt. jg. when his vessel, the Ka'Brough, ambushed and destroyed a Federation Battle Cruiser. True to their nature, Starfleet claimed the vessel was a luxury liner.

A year later, Krell met a young officer named Ensign A'Lan Vestai Vax. She had just reported to the Ka'Broug as their new Security Specialist. An intimate relationship grew between them. They mated after five months. Ensign A'Lan was brought into the House of Reshtarc. A year and a half later, the couple had their first child, the boy Leg'Ta.

During this time, Admiral Koll took a position at Southwatch University as Thought-Master for a newly opened Restricted Officers Training Corp. By this time the House of Reshtarc had opened a new door in the war business, biological warfare. The venture was called Southwatch Pest and Cleansing Company. In 19 years it expanded to nine different locations, including one on NgoKnuur itself.

By the time Leg'Ta was 19, he had two brothers and a sister. His brothers were Gor'Ge and Rhambata; his only sister was Brine. Tragically, Rhambata suffered from a mental deficiency. He was mercifully put to sleep. A'Lan and Krell never again spoke of Rhambata.

When Leg'Ta came of age, he entered the Imperial Star Academy, as had his father and grandfather. During his first year, his Grandmother, Parania, was injured in a shuttle accident. She died hours after arriving at the New Kaiy City medical facility.

Gor'Ge stayed closer to home, learning strategy and tactics as well as military history.

Cadet Leg'Ta majored in weapons defense and minored in security. Both Reshtarc boys graduated in the top 10% of their classes.

Leg'Ta and Gor'Ge received commissions in the Imperial Nguu Navy. Their sister Brine went to Southern Imperial College to major in communications and Komerexian literature. She pursued a career in Public Relations and Civil Propaganda with the Reshtarc Industries. Like her brothers, she graduated with top honors.

During his first tour of duty on the IKV Maska, Lt. jg. Leg'Ta received word of the illness of his grandfather, Admiral Koll Zantai Reshtarc. The Admiral was stricken with colon cancer. He died at the age of 88, after three unsuccessful operations. Admiral Kuller, a long time member of the Imperial High Council, soon followed, dead from a massive heart attack. He was also in his eighties.

Gor'Ge became an executive officer on the Nguu Cruiser IKV Drom'Kue, a D-7 Mako Class Battle Cruiser. Brine became Director of Civic Propaganda Department for the Reshtarc Industries. At the age of 24, she bonded with Jaab Sutai Solerzarn, and obtained the status of Vestai in the House of Solerzarn. A year later they had a child. They named the boy after a Great-Great Uncle Torn, who had died at the battle of Kobek. Jaab is a human/Nguu fusion, employed with Reshtarc Industries as Chief Engineer with Sensors and Phaser Weaponry Development department.

Today Admiral Krell is Epetai. He took over his uncle's duties as chief patriarch of the House of Reshtarc. A'Lan, his mate, gave up a military career to teach in the education system. She is now on the Board of Skill Masters for the entire Southwatch School System.

Lt. Leg'Ta Sutai Reshtarc now serves in the Nguu Strike Force as a Defensive Weapons Specialist in the Covert Operations Command. The populace of the House of Reshtarc has grown to over 30 thousand.

Not all members of the Reshtarc House are mentioned in this chapter, only the blood members to Reshtarc, with the exception of mates absorbed into the line, and important Epetais. The House of Reshtarc is growing and making their presence felt on the home world and in the Imperial Nguu Navy through its industries and higher education. They have given the Imperial Navy many top-quality officers, thereby maintaining the greater glory of the Nguu Empire.

THE MAN WHO CREATED STAR TREK: GENE RODDENBERRY

James Van Hise

The complete life story of the man who created STAR TREK, reveals the man and his work.

$14.95 in stores ONLY $12.95 to Couch Potato Catalog Customers
160 Pages
ISBN # 1-55698-318-2

TWENTY-FIFTH ANNIVERSARY TREK TRIBUTE

James Van Hise

Taking a close up look at the amazing Star Trek stroy, this book traces the history of the show that has become an enduring legend. James Van Hise chronicles the series from 1966 to its cancellation in 1969, through the years when only the fans kept it alive, and on to its unprecedented revival. He offers a look at its latter-day blossoming into an animated series, a sequence of five movies (with a sixth in preparation) that has grossed over $700 million, and the offshoot "The Next Generation" TV series.

The author gives readers a tour of the memorials at the Smithsonian and the Movieland Wax Museums, lets them witness Leonard Nimoy get his star on the Hollywood Walk Of Fame in 1985, and takes them behind the scenes of the motion-picture series and TV's "The Next Generation." The concluding section examines the future of Star Trek beyond its 25th Anniversary.

$14.95.....196 Pages
ISBN # 1-55698-290-9

BORING, BUT NECESSARY ORDERING INFORMATION

Payment:
Use our new 800 # and pay with your credit card or send check or money order directly to our address. All payments must be made in U.S. funds and please do not send cash.

Shipping:
We offer several methods of shipment. Sometimes a book can be delayed if we are temporarily out of stock. You should note whether you prefer us to ship the book as soon as available, send you a merchandise credit good for other goodies, or send your money back immediately.

Normal Post Office: $3.75 for the first book and $1.50 for each additional book. These orders are filled as quickly as possible. Shipments normally take 5 to 10 days, but allow up to 12 weeks for delivery.

Special UPS 2 Day Blue Label Service or Priority Mail: Special service is available for desperate Couch Potatoes. These books are shipped within 24 hours of when we receive the order and normally take 2 to 3 three days to get to you. The cost is $10.00 for the first book and $4.00 each additional book .

Overnight Rush Service: $20.00 for the first book and $10.00 each additional book.

U.s. Priority Mail: $6.00 for the first book and $3.00.each additional book.

Canada And Mexico: $5.00 for the first book and $3.00 each additional book.

Foreign: $6.00 for the first book and $3.00 each additional book.

Please list alternatives when available and please state if you would like a refund or for us to backorder an item if it is not in stock.

COUCH POTATO INC. 5715 N. Balsam Rd Las Vegas, NV 89130 (702)658-2090

Use Your Credit Card 24 HRS — Order toll Free From: **(800)444-2524** Ext 67

ORDER FORM

_____ Trek Crew Book $9.95
_____ Best Of Enterprise Incidents $9.95
_____ Trek Fans Handbook $9.95
_____ Trek: The Next Generation $14.95
_____ The Man Who Created Star Trek: $12.95
_____ 25th Anniversary Trek Tribute $14.95
_____ History Of Trek $14.95
_____ The Man Between The Ears $14.95
_____ Trek: The Making Of The Movies $14.95
_____ Trek: The Lost Years $12.95
_____ Trek: The Unauthorized Next Generation $14.95
_____ New Trek Encyclopedia $19.95
_____ Making A Quantum Leap $14.95
_____ The Unofficial Tale Of Beauty And The Beast $14.95
_____ Complete Lost In Space $19.95
_____ ..doctor Who Encyclopedia: Baker $19.95
_____ Lost In Space Tribute Book $14.95
_____ Lost In Space With Irwin Allen $14.95
_____ Doctor Who: Baker Years $19.95
_____ Doctor Who: Pertwee Years $19.95
_____ Batmania Ii $14.95
_____ The Green Hornet $14.95 _____ Special Edition $16.95

_____ Number Six: The Prisoner Book $14.95
_____ Gerry Anderson: Supermarionation $17.95
_____ Addams Family Revealed $14.95
_____ Bloodsucker: Vampires At The Movies $14.95
_____ Dark Shadows Tribute $14.95
_____ Monsterland Fear Book $14.95
_____ The Films Of Elvis $14.95
_____ The Woody Allen Encyclopedia $14.95
_____ Paul Mccartney: 20 Years On His Own $9.95
_____ Yesterday: My Life With The Beatles $14.95
_____ Fab Films Of The Beatles $14.95
_____ 40 Years At Night: The Tonight Show $14.95
_____ Exposing Northern Exposure $14.95
_____ The La Lawbook $14.95
_____ Cheers: Where Everybody Knows Your Name $14.95
_____ SNL! The World Of Saturday Night Live $14.95
_____ The Rockford Phile $14.95
_____ Encyclopedia Of Cartoon Superstars $14.95
_____ How To Create Animation $14.95
_____ How To Draw Art For Comic Books $14.95
_____ King And Barker:an Illustrated Guide $14.95
_____ King And Barker: An Illustrated Guide II $14.95

100% Satisfaction Guaranteed.

We value your support. You will receive a full refund as long as the copy of the book you are not happy with is received back by us in reasonable condition. No questions asked, except we would like to know how we failed you. Refunds and credits are given as soon as we receive back the item you do not want.

NAME:_____

STREET:_____

CITY:_____

STATE:_____

ZIP:_____

TOTAL:_____ SHIPPING_____

SEND TO: Couch Potato, Inc. 5715 N. Balsam Rd., Las Vegas, NV 89130